www.EffortlessMath.com

... So Much More Online!

✓ FREE Math lessons

✓ More Math learning books!

✓ Mathematics Worksheets

✓ Online Math Tutors

Need a PDF version of this book?

Please visit www.EffortlessMath.com

ALEKS Math Preparation 2020 - 2021

ALEKS Math Workbook + 2 Full-Length ALEKS Math Practice Tests

By

Reza Nazari & Ava Ross

Copyright © 2020

Reza Nazari & Ava Ross

All inquiries should be addressed to:

info@effortlessMath.com

www.EffortlessMath.com

ISBN: 978-1-64612-895-2

Published by: Effortless Math Education

www.EffortlessMath.com

Description

ALEKS Math Preparation 2020 - 2021, which reflects the 2020 - 2021 test guidelines, is prepared by top ALEKS instructors and test prep experts to help test takers succeed on the ALEKS Math Test. This ALEKS Math prep new edition has been updated to replicate questions appearing on the most recent ALEKS Math tests. Upon completion of this comprehensive ALEKS Math prep book, you will have a solid foundation and sufficient practice to ace the ALEKS Math test. **This prep book is your ticket to scoring higher on ALEKS Math.**

Not only does this perfect and comprehensive ALEKS Math book include everything you will ever need to conquer the ALEKS Math test, but it also contains two full-length and realistic ALEKS Math practice tests that reflect the format and question types on the ALEKS to help you check your exam-readiness and identify where you need more practice.

ALEKS Math Preparation 2020 - 2021 contains many exciting and unique features to help you improve your test scores, including:

- ✓ Content 100% aligned with the 2020 ALEKS® test
- ✓ Complete coverage of all ALEKS Math concepts which you will be tested
- ✓ Numerous Quantitative Reasoning practice questions in both multiple-choice and grid-in formats with answers grouped by topic, so you can focus on your weak areas
- ✓ Abundant Math skill-building exercises to help test-takers approach different question types that might be unfamiliar to them
- ✓ 2 full-length practice tests (featuring new question types) with detailed answers

This ALEKS Math prep book and other Effortless Math Education books are used by thousands of students each year to help them review core content areas, brush-up in math, discover their strengths and weaknesses, and achieve their best scores on the ALEKS test.

About the Author

Reza Nazari is the author of more than 100 Math learning books including:
– **Math and Critical Thinking Challenges:** For the Middle and High School Student
– **GED Math in 30 Days**
– **ASVAB Math Workbook 2018 - 2019**
– **Effortless Math Education Workbooks**
– **and many more Mathematics books …**

Reza is also an experienced Math instructor and a test–prep expert who has been tutoring students since 2008. Reza is the founder of Effortless Math Education, a tutoring company that has helped many students raise their standardized test scores—and attend the colleges of their dreams. Reza provides an individualized custom learning plan and the personalized attention that makes a difference in how students view math.

You can contact Reza via email at:
reza@EffortlessMath.com

Find Reza's professional profile at:
goo.gl/zoC9rJ

Contents

Chapter 1:

Fractions and Mixed Numbers

Topics that you'll practice in this chapter:

✓ Simplifying Fractions

✓ Adding and Subtracting Fractions

✓ Multiplying and Dividing Fractions

✓ Adding Mixed Numbers

✓ Subtracting Mixed Numbers

✓ Multiplying Mixed Numbers

✓ Dividing Mixed Numbers

Name:	Date: ....

Topic	*Simplifying Fractions*	
Notes	✓ Evenly divide both the top and bottom of the fraction by $2, 3, 5, 7, \ldots$ etc. ✓ Continue until you can't go any further.	
Example	*Simplify* $\frac{36}{48}$ **Solution:** To simplify $\frac{36}{48}$, find a number that both 36 and 48 are divisible by. Both are divisible by 12. Then: $\frac{36}{48} = \frac{36 \div 12}{48 \div 12} = \frac{3}{4}$	
Your Turn!	1) $\frac{2}{18} =$	2) $\frac{22}{66} =$
	3) $\frac{12}{48} =$	4) $\frac{11}{99} =$
	5) $\frac{15}{75} =$	6) $\frac{25}{100} =$
	7) $\frac{16}{72} =$	8) $\frac{32}{96} =$
	9) $\frac{14}{77} =$	10) $\frac{60}{84} =$

| **Name:** .... | **Date:** .... |

Topic	*Adding and Subtracting Fractions*
Notes	✓ For "like" fractions (fractions with the same denominator), add or subtract the numerators and write the answer over the common denominator. ✓ Find equivalent fractions with the same denominator before you can add or subtract fractions with different denominators. ✓ Adding and Subtracting with the same denominator: $$\frac{a}{b}+\frac{c}{b}=\frac{a+c}{b}\ ,\frac{a}{b}-\frac{c}{b}=\frac{a-c}{b}$$ ✓ Adding and Subtracting fractions with different denominators: $$\frac{a}{b}+\frac{c}{d}=\frac{ad+bc}{bd},\frac{a}{b}-\frac{c}{d}=\frac{ad-bc}{bd}$$
Example	1) *Find* the sum. $\frac{3}{5}+\frac{2}{3}$ Solution: $\frac{3}{5}+\frac{2}{3}=\frac{(3)3+(5)(2)}{5\times3}=\frac{19}{15}$ 2) *Subtract.* $\frac{4}{7}-\frac{3}{7}$ Solution: $\frac{4}{7}-\frac{3}{7}=\frac{1}{7}$
Your Turn!	1) $\frac{3}{5}+\frac{2}{7}=$ 2) $\frac{7}{9}-\frac{4}{7}=$ 3) $\frac{4}{9}+\frac{5}{8}=$ 4) $\frac{5}{8}-\frac{2}{5}=$ 5) $\frac{2}{5}+\frac{1}{6}=$ 6) $\frac{2}{3}-\frac{1}{4}=$ 7) $\frac{8}{9}+\frac{5}{7}=$ 8) $\frac{6}{7}-\frac{5}{9}=$

Name:	Date: ....

Topic	*Multiplying and Dividing Fractions*
Notes	✓ Multiplying fractions: multiply the top numbers and multiply the bottom numbers. ✓ Dividing fractions: Keep, Change, Flip Keep first fraction, change division sign to multiplication, and flip the numerator and denominator of the second fraction. Then, solve!
Examples	1) *Multiply.* $\frac{2}{5} \times \frac{3}{4} =$ **Solution:** Multiply the top numbers and multiply the bottom numbers. $\frac{2}{5} \times \frac{3}{4} = \frac{2 \times 3}{5 \times 4} = \frac{6}{20}$, simplify: $\frac{6}{2} = \frac{6 \div 2}{20 \div 2} = \frac{3}{10}$ 2) *Divide.* $\frac{2}{5} \div \frac{3}{4} =$ **Solution:** Keep first fraction, change division sign to multiplication, and flip the numerator and denominator of the second fraction. Then: $\frac{2}{5} \div \frac{3}{4} = \frac{2}{5} \times \frac{4}{3} = \frac{2 \times 4}{5 \times 3} = \frac{8}{15}$
Your Turn!	1) $\frac{5}{9} \times \frac{4}{7} =$ 2) $\frac{3}{5} \div \frac{2}{3} =$ 3) $\frac{2}{7} \times \frac{3}{5} =$ 4) $\frac{2}{5} \div \frac{7}{12} =$ 5) $\frac{1}{7} \times \frac{4}{9} =$ 6) $\frac{2}{9} \div \frac{3}{7} =$ 7) $\frac{2}{5} \times \frac{6}{7} =$ 8) $\frac{1}{4} \div \frac{2}{5} =$

Name: ....   Date: ....

Topic	*Adding Mixed Numbers*
Notes	Use the following steps for adding mixed numbers. ✓ Add whole numbers of the mixed numbers. ✓ Add the fractions of each mixed number. ✓ Find the Least Common Denominator (LCD) if necessary. ✓ Add whole numbers and fractions. ✓ Write your answer in lowest terms.
Example	*Add mixed numbers.* $1\frac{1}{2} + 2\frac{2}{3} =$ **Solution:** Rewriting our equation with parts separated, $1 + \frac{1}{2} + 2 + \frac{2}{3}$ Add whole numbers: $1 + 2 = 3$ Add fractions: $\frac{1}{2} + \frac{2}{3} = \frac{3}{6} + \frac{4}{6} = \frac{7}{6} = 1\frac{1}{6}$, Now, combine the whole and fraction parts: $3 + 1 + \frac{1}{6} = 4\frac{1}{6}$
Your Turn!	1) $1\frac{1}{12} + 2\frac{3}{4} =$ 2) $3\frac{5}{8} + 1\frac{1}{4} =$ 3) $1\frac{1}{10} + 2\frac{2}{5} =$ 4) $2\frac{5}{6} + 2\frac{2}{9} =$ 5) $2\frac{2}{7} + 1\frac{2}{21} =$ 6) $1\frac{3}{8} + 3\frac{2}{3} =$ 7) $3\frac{1}{5} + 1\frac{2}{8} =$ 8) $3\frac{1}{2} + 2\frac{3}{7} =$

| Name: .... | Date: .... |

Topic	**_Subtracting Mixed Numbers_**
Notes	Use the following steps for subtracting mixed numbers. ✓ Convert mixed numbers into improper fractions. $a\frac{c}{b} = \frac{ab+c}{b}$ ✓ Find equivalent fractions with the same denominator for unlike fractions (fractions with different denominators) ✓ Subtract the second fraction from the first one. ✓ Write your answer in lowest terms and convert it into a mixed number if the answer is an improper fraction.
Example	_Subtract._ $5\frac{1}{2} - 2\frac{2}{3} =$ **Solution:** Convert mixed numbers into fractions: $5\frac{1}{2} = \frac{5\times2+1}{5} = \frac{11}{2}$ and $2\frac{2}{3} = \frac{2\times3+2}{4} = \frac{8}{3}$, these two fractions are "unlike" fractions. (they have different denominators). Find equivalent fractions with the same denominator. Use this formula: $\frac{a}{b} - \frac{c}{d} = \frac{ad-bc}{bd}$ $\frac{11}{2} - \frac{8}{3} = \frac{(11)(3)-(2)(8)}{2\times3} = \frac{33-16}{6} = \frac{17}{6}$, the answer is an improper fraction, convert it into a mixed number. $\frac{17}{6} = 2\frac{5}{6}$
Your Turn!	1) $2\frac{2}{5} - 1\frac{1}{3} =$
	3) $6\frac{1}{4} - 1\frac{2}{7} =$
	5) $8\frac{3}{4} - 1\frac{3}{8} =$
	7) $13\frac{2}{7} - 1\frac{2}{21} =$

1) $2\frac{2}{5} - 1\frac{1}{3} =$	2) $3\frac{5}{8} - 2\frac{1}{3} =$
3) $6\frac{1}{4} - 1\frac{2}{7} =$	4) $8\frac{2}{3} - 1\frac{1}{4} =$
5) $8\frac{3}{4} - 1\frac{3}{8} =$	6) $2\frac{3}{8} - 1\frac{2}{3} =$
7) $13\frac{2}{7} - 1\frac{2}{21} =$	8) $5\frac{1}{2} - 2\frac{3}{7} =$

Name: ....

Date: ....

Topic	*Multiplying Mixed Numbers*
Notes	✓ Convert the mixed numbers into fractions. $a\frac{c}{b} = a + \frac{c}{b} = \frac{ab+c}{b}$ ✓ Multiply fractions and simplify if necessary. $\frac{a}{b} \times \frac{c}{d} = \frac{a \times c}{b \times d}$ ✓ If the answer is an improper fraction (numerator is bigger than denominator), convert it into a mixed number.
Example	*Multiply* $2\frac{1}{4} \times 3\frac{1}{2}$ **Solution:** Convert mixed numbers into fractions: $2\frac{1}{4} = \frac{2 \times 4 + 1}{4} = \frac{9}{4}$ and $3\frac{1}{2} = \frac{3 \times 2 + 1}{2} = \frac{7}{2}$ Multiply two fractions: $\frac{9}{4} \times \frac{7}{2} = \frac{9 \times 7}{4 \times 2} = \frac{63}{8}$ The answer is an improper fraction. Convert it into a mixed number: $$\frac{63}{8} = 7\frac{7}{8}$$
Your Turn!	1) $5\frac{2}{3} \times 2\frac{2}{9} =$ 2) $4\frac{1}{6} \times 5\frac{3}{7} =$ 3) $3\frac{1}{3} \times 3\frac{3}{4} =$ 4) $2\frac{2}{9} \times 6\frac{1}{3} =$ 5) $2\frac{2}{7} \times 4\frac{3}{5} =$ 6) $1\frac{4}{7} \times 9\frac{1}{2} =$ 7) $4\frac{1}{8} \times 3\frac{2}{3} =$ 8) $6\frac{2}{3} \times 1\frac{1}{4} =$

Name: ....   **Date:** ....

Topic	***Dividing Mixed Numbers***
Notes	✓ Convert the mixed numbers into improper fractions. $$a\frac{c}{b} = a + \frac{c}{b} = \frac{ab+c}{b}$$ ✓ Divide fractions and simplify if necessary.
Example	*Solve.* $2\frac{1}{3} \div 1\frac{1}{4} =$ **Solution:** Converting mixed numbers to fractions: $2\frac{1}{3} \div 1\frac{1}{4} = \frac{7}{3} \div \frac{5}{4}$ Keep, Change, Flip: $\frac{7}{3} \div \frac{5}{4} = \frac{7}{3} \times \frac{4}{5} = \frac{7 \times 4}{3 \times 5} = \frac{28}{15} = 1\frac{13}{15}$

Your Turn!	1) $3\frac{2}{7} \div 2\frac{1}{4} =$	2) $4\frac{2}{9} \div 1\frac{5}{6} =$
	3) $4\frac{2}{3} \div 3\frac{2}{5} =$	4) $5\frac{4}{5} \div 4\frac{3}{4} =$
	5) $1\frac{8}{9} \div 2\frac{3}{7} =$	6) $3\frac{3}{8} \div 2\frac{2}{5} =$
	7) $4\frac{1}{5} \div 3\frac{1}{9} =$	8) $4\frac{2}{3} \div 1\frac{8}{9} =$
	9) $5\frac{2}{3} \div 3\frac{3}{7} =$	10) $7\frac{1}{2} \div 5\frac{1}{3} =$

Answers – Chapter 1

Simplifying Fractions

1) $\frac{1}{9}$

2) $\frac{1}{3}$

3) $\frac{1}{4}$

4) $\frac{1}{9}$

5) $\frac{1}{5}$

6) $\frac{1}{4}$

7) $\frac{2}{9}$

8) $\frac{1}{3}$

9) $\frac{2}{11}$

10) $\frac{5}{7}$

Adding and Subtracting Fractions

1) $\frac{31}{35}$

2) $\frac{13}{63}$

3) $\frac{77}{72}$

4) $\frac{9}{40}$

5) $\frac{17}{30}$

6) $\frac{5}{12}$

7) $\frac{101}{63}$

8) $\frac{19}{63}$

Multiplying and Dividing Fractions

1) $\frac{20}{63}$

2) $\frac{9}{10}$

3) $\frac{6}{35}$

4) $\frac{24}{35}$

5) $\frac{4}{63}$

6) $\frac{14}{27}$

7) $\frac{12}{35}$

8) $\frac{5}{8}$

Adding Mixed Numbers

1) $3\frac{5}{6}$

2) $4\frac{7}{8}$

3) $3\frac{1}{2}$

4) $5\frac{1}{18}$

5) $3\frac{8}{21}$

6) $5\frac{1}{24}$

7) $4\frac{9}{20}$

8) $5\frac{13}{14}$

Subtracting Mixed Numbers

1) $1\frac{1}{15}$

2) $1\frac{7}{24}$

3) $4\frac{27}{28}$

4) $7\frac{5}{12}$

5) $7\frac{3}{8}$

6) $\frac{17}{24}$

7) $12\frac{4}{21}$

8) $3\frac{1}{4}$

Multiplying Mixed Numbers

1) $12\frac{16}{27}$

2) $22\frac{13}{21}$

3) $12\frac{1}{2}$

4) $14\frac{2}{27}$

5) $10\frac{18}{35}$

6) $14\frac{13}{14}$

7) $15\frac{1}{8}$

8) $8\frac{1}{3}$

Dividing Mixed numbers

1) $1\frac{29}{63}$

2) $2\frac{10}{33}$

3) $1\frac{19}{51}$

4) $1\frac{21}{95}$

5) $\frac{7}{9}$

6) $1\frac{13}{32}$

7) $1\frac{7}{20}$

8) $2\frac{8}{17}$

9) $1\frac{47}{72}$

10) $1\frac{13}{32}$

Chapter 2:

Decimals

Topics that you'll practice in this chapter:

- ✓ Comparing Decimals
- ✓ Rounding Decimals
- ✓ Adding and Subtracting Decimals
- ✓ Multiplying and Dividing Decimals

Name: ……………………………………….

Date: ……………………………………..

Topic	*Comparing Decimals*
Notes	Decimals: is a fraction written in a special form. For example, instead of writing $\frac{1}{2}$ you can write **0. 5**. For comparing decimals: ✓ Compare each digit of two decimals in the same place value. ✓ Start from left. Compare hundreds, tens, ones, tenth, hundredth, etc. ✓ To compare numbers, use these symbols: - Equal to $=$, Less than $<$, Greater than $>$ Greater than or equal $\geq$, Less than or equal $\leq$
Examples	1) Compare 0.40 and 0.04. **Solution:** 0.40 *is greater than* 0.04, because the tenth place of 0.40 is 4, but the tenth place of 0.04 is zero. Then: $0.40 > 0.04$ 2) Compare 0.0912 and 0.912. **Solution:** 0.912 *is greater than* 0.0912, because the tenth place of 0.912 is 9, but the tenth place of 0.0912 is zero. Then: $0.0912 < 0.912$

Your Turn!

1) $0.91 \square 0.95$	2) $1.79 \square 1.80$
3) $19.1 \square 19.09$	4) $2.45 \square 2.089$
5) $1.258 \square 12.58$	6) $0.89 \square 0.890$
7) $3.871 \square 2.998$	8) $0.567 \square 0.756$

Name:	Date: ....

Topic	*Rounding Decimals*
Notes	✓ We can round decimals to a certain accuracy or number of decimal places. ✓ Let's review place values: For example: **35.4817** 3: tens 5: ones 4: tenths 8: hundredths 1: thousandths 7:tens thousandths ✓ To round a decimal, find the place value you'll round to. ✓ Find the digit to the right of the place value you're rounding to. If it is 5 or bigger, add 1 to the place value you're rounding to and remove all digits on its right side. If the digit to the right of the place value is less than 5, keep the place value and remove all digits on the right.
Example	Round **12.8365** to the hundredth place value. First look at the next place value to the right, (thousandths). It's 6 and it is greater than 5. Thus add 1 to the digit in the hundredth place. It is 3. $\rightarrow$ 3 + 1 = 4, then, the answer is 12.84
Your Turn!	Round each number to the *underlined* place value. 1) 32.5_4_8 = 2) 2.3_2_6 = 3) 55._4_23 = 4) 2_5_.62 = 5) 11._2_65 = 6) 33.5_0_5 = 7) 3.5_8_9 = 8) 8.0_1_9 =

Name:	Date: ....

Topic	*Adding and Subtracting Decimals*
Notes	✓ Line up the numbers. ✓ Add zeros to have same number of digits for both numbers if necessary. ✓ Add or subtract using column addition or subtraction.
Examples	1) *Add*. $2.6 + 5.33 =$ **Solution:** First line up the numbers: $\begin{array}{r} 2.6 \\ + 5.33 \\ \hline \end{array}$ →Add zeros to have same number of digits for both numbers. $\begin{array}{r} 2.60 \\ + 5.33 \\ \hline \end{array}$ → Start with the hundredths place. $0 + 3 =$ $2, \begin{array}{r} 2.60 \\ + 5.33 \\ \hline 3 \end{array}$ → Continue with tenths place. $6 + 3 = 9, \begin{array}{r} 2.60 \\ + 5.33 \\ \hline .93 \end{array}$ → Add the ones place. $2 + 5 = 7, \begin{array}{r} 2.60 \\ + 5.33 \\ \hline 7.93 \end{array}$ 2) *Subtract*. $4.79 - 3.13 = \begin{array}{r} 4.79 \\ - 3.13 \\ \hline \end{array}$ **Solution:** Start with the hundredths place. $9 - 3 = 6, \begin{array}{r} 4.79 \\ - 3.13 \\ \hline 6 \end{array}$, continue with tenths place. $7 - 1 = 6, \begin{array}{r} 4.79 \\ - 3.13 \\ \hline .66 \end{array}$, subtract the ones place. $4 - 3 = 1, \begin{array}{r} 4.79 \\ - 3.13 \\ \hline 1.66 \end{array}$
Your Turn!	1) $48.13 + 20.15 =$ 2) $78.14 - 65.19 =$ 3) $38.19 + 24.18 =$ 4) $57.26 - 43.54 =$ 5) $27.89 + 46.13 =$ 6) $49.65 - 32.78 =$

Name: ....

Date: ....

Topic	*Multiplying and Dividing Decimals*
Notes	For Multiplication: ✓ Ignore the decimal point and set up and multiply the numbers as you do with whole numbers. ✓ Count the total number of decimal places in both factors. ✓ Place the decimal point in the product. For Division: ✓ If the divisor is not a whole number, move decimal point to right to make it a whole number. Do the same for dividend. ✓ Divide similar to whole numbers.
Examples	1) Find the product. $1.2 \times 2.3 =$ **Solution:** Set up and multiply the numbers as you do with whole numbers. Line up the numbers: $\frac{12}{\times 23}$ → Multiply: $\frac{12}{\frac{\times 23}{276}}$ → Count the total number of decimal places in both of the factors. There are two decimal digits. Then: $1.2 \times 2.3 = 2.76$ 2) Find the quotient. $5.6 \div 0.8 =$ **Solution:** The divisor is not a whole number. Multiply it by 10 to get 8. → $0.8 \times 10 = 8$ Do the same for the dividend to get 56 → $5.6 \times 10 = 56$ Now, divide: $56 \div 8 = 7$. The answer is 7.
Your Turn!	1) $1.13 \times 0.7 =$ 2) $48.8 \div 8 =$ 3) $0.9 \times 0.68 =$ 4) $66.8 \div 0.2 =$ 5) $0.18 \times 0.5 =$ 6) $37.2 \div 100 =$

Answers – Chapter 2

Comparing Decimals

1) <
2) <
3) >
4) >

5) <
6) =
7) >
8) <

Rounding Decimals

1) 32.25
2) 2.33
3) 55.4
4) 26

5) 11.3
6) 33.51
7) 3.59
8) 8.02

Adding and Subtracting Decimals

1) 68.28
2) 12.95
3) 62.37

4) 13.72
5) 74.02
6) 16.87

Multiplying and Dividing Decimals

1) 0.791
2) 6.1
3) 0.612

4) 334
5) 0.09
6) 0.372

Chapter 3:

Integers and Order of Operations

Topics that you'll practice in this chapter:

✓ Adding and Subtracting Integers

✓ Multiplying and Dividing Integers

✓ Order of Operations

✓ Integers and Absolute Value

Name:	Date: ....

Topic	*Adding and Subtracting Integers*	
Notes	✓ Integers include: zero, counting numbers, and the negative of the counting numbers. $\{... , -3, -2, -1, 0, 1, 2, 3, ...\}$ ✓ Add a positive integer by moving to the right on the number line. ✓ Add a negative integer by moving to the left on the number line. Subtract an integer by adding its opposite.	
Examples	1) Solve. $(4) - (-8) =$ **Solution:** Keep the first number and convert the sign of the second number to its opposite. (change subtraction into addition. Then: $(4) + 8 = 12$ 2) Solve. $42 + (12 - 26) =$ **Solution:** First subtract the numbers in brackets, $12 - 26 = -14$ Then: $42 + (-14) = \rightarrow$ change addition into subtraction: $42 - 14 = 28$	
Your Turn!	1) $-(15) + 12 =$	2) $(-2) + (-10) + 18 =$
	3) $(-13) + 7 =$	4) $3 - (-7) + 14 =$
	5) $(-7) + (-8) =$	6) $16 - (-4 + 8) =$
	7) $4 + (-15) + 2 =$	8) $-(22) - (-4) + 8 =$

Name: ....

Date: ....

Topic	*Multiplying and Dividing Integers*
Notes	Use following rules for multiplying and dividing integers: ✓ (negative) × (negative) = positive ✓ (negative) ÷ (negative) = positive ✓ (negative) × (positive) = negative ✓ (negative) ÷ (positive) = negative ✓ (positive) × (positive) = positive ✓ (positive) ÷ (negative) = negative
Examples	1) Solve. $2 \times (14 - 17) =$ **Solution:** First subtract the numbers in brackets, $14 - 17 = -3 \rightarrow$ $(2) \times (-3) =$ Now use this rule: (positive) × (negative) = negative $(2) \times (-3) = -6$ 2) Solve. $(-7) + (-36 \div 4) =$ **Solution:** First divide -36 by 4 , the numbers in brackets, using this rule: (negative) ÷ (positive) = negative Then: $-36 \div 4 = -9$. Now, add -7 and -9: $(-7) + (-9) = -7 - 9 = -16$
Your Turn!	1) $(-7) \times 6 =$ 2) $(-63) \div (-7) =$ 3) $(-11) \times (-3) =$ 4) $81 \div (-9) =$ 5) $(15 - 12) \times (-7) =$ 6) $(-12) \div (3) =$ 7) $4 \times (-9) =$ 8) $(8) \div (-2) =$

Name: ....

Date: ....

Topic	*Order of Operation*
Notes	When there is more than one math operation, use PEMDAS: (to memorize this rule, remember the phrase "Please Excuse My Dear Aunt Sally") ✓ Parentheses ✓ Exponents ✓ Multiplication and Division (from left to right) ✓ Addition and Subtraction (from left to right)
Examples	1) Calculate. $(18 - 26) \div (2^4 \div 4) =$ **Solution:** First simplify inside parentheses: $(-8) \div (16 \div 4) = (-8) \div (4)$ Then: $(-8) \div (4) = -2$ 2) Solve. $(-5 \times 7) - (18 - 3^2) =$ **Solution:** First calculate within parentheses: $(-5 \times 7) - (18 - 3^2) =$ $(-35) - (18 - 9)$ Then: $(-35) - (18 - 9) = -35 - 9 = -44$

Your Turn!		
	1) $(11 \times 4) \div (5 + 6) =$	2) $(30 \div 5) + (17 - 8) =$
	3) $(-9) + (5 \times 6) + 14 =$	4) $(-10 \times 5) \div (2^2 + 1) =$
	5) $[-16(32 \div 2^3)] \div 8 =$	6) $(-7) + (72 \div 3^2) + 12 =$
	7) $[16(32 \div 2^3)] - 4^2 =$	8) $4^3 + (-5 \times 2^5) + 5 =$

Name: ....

Date: ....

Topic	*Integers and Absolute Value*
Notes	✓ The absolute value of a number is its distance from zero, in either direction, on the number line. For example, the distance of 9 and -9 from zero on number line is 9. ✓ Absolute value is symbolized by vertical bars, as in $\|x\|$.
Example	Calculate. $\|8-5\| \times \|12-16\| =$ **Solution:** First calculate $\|8-5\|$, $\rightarrow \|8-5\| = \|3\|$, the absolute value of 3 is 3, $\|3\| = 3$ $8 \times \|12-16\| =$ Now calculate $\|12-16\|$, $\rightarrow \|12-16\| = \|-4\|$, the absolute value of -4 is 4, $\|-4\| = 4$. Then: $3 \times 4 = 12$

Your Turn!	
1) $11 - \|4-13\| =$	2) $14 - \|12-19\| - \|9\| =$
3) $\|21\| - \dfrac{\|-25\|}{5} =$	4) $\|30\| + \dfrac{\|-49\|}{7} =$
5) $\dfrac{\|7 \times -8\|}{4} \times \dfrac{\|-12\|}{2} =$	6) $\dfrac{\|10 \times -6\|}{5} \times \|-9\| =$
7) $\dfrac{\|-20\|}{5} \times \dfrac{\|-36\|}{6} =$	8) $\|-30+6\| \times \dfrac{\|-9 \times 4\|}{12} =$

Answers– Chapter 3

Adding and Subtracting Integers

1) −3
2) 6
3) −6

4) 24
5) −15
6) 12

7) −9
8) −10

Multiplying and Dividing Integers

1) −42
2) 9
3) 33

4) −9
5) −21
6) −4

7) −36
8) −4

Order of Operations

1) 4
2) 15
3) 35

4) −10
5) −8
6) 13

7) 48
8) −91

Integers and Absolute Value

1) 2
2) −2
3) 16

4) 37
5) 84
6) 108

7) 24
8) 72

Chapter 4:

Ratios and Proportions

Math Topics that you'll learn in this Chapter:

✓ Simplifying Ratios

✓ Proportional Ratios

✓ Create Proportion

✓ Similarity and Ratios

✓ Simple Interest

Name: ....   **Date:** ....

Topic	*Simplifying Ratios*	
Notes	✓ Ratios are used to make comparisons between two numbers. ✓ Ratios can be written as a fraction, using the word "to", or with a colon. ✓ You can calculate equivalent ratios by multiplying or dividing both sides of the ratio by the same number.	
Examples	1) Simplify. $18:63 =$ **Solution:** Both numbers 18 and 63 are divisible by $9 \Rightarrow 18 \div 9 = 2$, $63 \div 9 = 7$, Then: $18:63 = 2:7$ 2) Simplify. $\frac{25}{45} =$ **Solution:** Both numbers 25 and 45 are divisible by 5, $\Rightarrow 25 \div 5 = 5$, $45 \div 5 = 9$, Then: $\frac{25}{45} = \frac{5}{9}$	
Your Turn!	1) $\frac{4}{32} = -$	2) $\frac{25}{80} = -$
	3) $\frac{15}{35} = -$	4) $\frac{42}{54} = -$
	5) $\frac{12}{36} = -$	6) $\frac{30}{80} = -$
	7) $\frac{18}{24} = -$	8) $\frac{60}{108} = -$

Name: ....   Date: ....

Topic	*Proportional Ratios*
Notes	✓ Two ratios are proportional if they represent the same relationship. ✓ A proportion means that two ratios are equal. It can be written in two ways: $\frac{a}{b} = \frac{c}{d}$ $a : b = c : d$
Example	Solve this proportion for x. $\frac{5}{8} = \frac{35}{x}$ **Solution:** Use cross multiplication: $\frac{5}{8} = \frac{35}{x} \Rightarrow 5 \times x = 8 \times 35 \Rightarrow$ $5x = 280$ Divide to find x: $x = \frac{280}{5} \Rightarrow x = 56$
Your Turn!	1) $\frac{1}{9} = \frac{8}{x} \Rightarrow x =$ _____ 2) $\frac{5}{8} = \frac{25}{x} \Rightarrow x =$ _____ 3) $\frac{3}{11} = \frac{6}{x} \Rightarrow x =$ _____ 4) $\frac{12}{20} = \frac{x}{200} \Rightarrow x =$ _____ 5) $\frac{9}{12} = \frac{27}{x} \Rightarrow x =$ _____ 6) $\frac{14}{16} = \frac{x}{80} \Rightarrow x =$ _____ 7) $\frac{7}{15} = \frac{49}{x} \Rightarrow x =$ _____ 8) $\frac{8}{19} = \frac{32}{x} \Rightarrow x =$ _____

Name:	Date: ....

Topic	*Create Proportion*
Notes	✓ To create a proportion, simply find (or create) two equal fractions. ✓ Use cross products to solve proportions or to test whether two ratios are equal and form a proportion. $\frac{a}{b} = \frac{c}{d} \Rightarrow a \times d = c \times b$
Example	***State if this pair of ratios form a proportion.*** $\frac{2}{3}$ *and* $\frac{12}{30}$ Use cross multiplication: $\frac{2}{3} = \frac{12}{30} \rightarrow 2 \times 30 = 12 \times 3 \rightarrow 60 = 36$, which is not correct. Therefore, this pair of ratios doesn't form a proportion.

State if each pair of ratios form a proportion.

1) $\frac{4}{8}$ and $\frac{24}{48}$	2) $\frac{5}{15}$ and $\frac{10}{20}$
3) $\frac{3}{11}$ and $\frac{9}{33}$	4) $\frac{7}{10}$ and $\frac{14}{20}$
5) $\frac{7}{9}$ and $\frac{48}{81}$	6) $\frac{6}{8}$ and $\frac{12}{14}$
7) $\frac{2}{10}$ and $\frac{6}{30}$	8) $\frac{9}{12}$ and $\frac{18}{24}$

Your Turn!

9) Solve.

Five pencils costs $0.65. How many pencils can you buy for $2.60? _____

Name: ....

Date: ....

Topic	*Similarity and Ratios*
Notes	✓ Two figures are similar if they have the same shape. ✓ Two or more figures are similar if the corresponding angles are equal, and the corresponding sides are in proportion.
Example	Following triangles are similar. What is the value of unknown side? **Solution:** Find the corresponding sides and write a proportion: $\frac{4}{12} = \frac{x}{9}$. Now, use cross product to solve for x: $\frac{4}{12} = \frac{x}{9} \rightarrow 4 \times 9 = 12 \times x \rightarrow 36 = 12x$. Divide both sides by 12. Then: $5x = 40 \rightarrow \frac{36}{12} = \frac{12x}{12} \rightarrow x = 3$. The missing side is 3.

Your Turn!	1) 2) 3) 4) 5) 6)

| Name: .... | Date: .... |

Topic	*Simple Interest*
Notes	✓ Simple Interest: The charge for borrowing money or the return for lending it. To solve a simple interest problem, use this formula: Interest = principal x rate x time $\Rightarrow$ $\boldsymbol{I = p \times r \times t}$
Example	Find simple interest for $3,000 investment at 5% for 4 years. **Solution:** Use Interest formula: $I = prt$ ($P = \$3,000$, r $= 5\% = 0.05$ and $t = 4$) Then: $I = 3,000 \times 0.05 \times 4 = \$600$
Your Turn!	1) $250 at 4% for 3 years. Simple interest: $_____ 2) $3,300 at 5% for 6 years. Simple interest: $_____ 3) $720 at 2% for 5 years. Simple interest: $_____ 4) $2,200 at 8% for 4 years. Simple interest: $_____ 5) $1,800 at 3% for 2 years. Simple interest: $_____ 6) $530 at 4% for 5 years. Simple interest: $_____ 7) $7,000 at 5% for 3 months. Simple interest: $_____ 8) $880 at 5% for 9 months. Simple interest: $_____

Answers– Chapter 4

Simplifying Ratios

1) $\frac{1}{8}$

2) $\frac{5}{16}$

3) $\frac{3}{7}$

4) $\frac{7}{9}$

5) $\frac{1}{3}$

6) $\frac{3}{8}$

7) $\frac{3}{4}$

8) $\frac{5}{9}$

Create Proportion

1) *Yes*

2) *No*

3) *Yes*

4) *Yes*

5) *No*

6) *No*

7) *Yes*

8) *Yes*

9) 20 pencils

Proportional Ratios

1) 72

2) 40

3) 22

4) 120

5) 36

6) 70

7) 105

8) 76

Similarity and ratios

1) 24

2) 11

3) 4

4) 8

5) 10

6) 9

Chapter 5:

Percentage

Math Topics that you'll learn in this Chapter:

✓ Percent Problems

✓ Percent of Increase and Decrease

✓ Discount, Tax and Tip

Name: ....

Date: ....

Topic	*Percent Problems*

Notes	✓ In each percent problem, we are looking for the base, or part or the percent.
	✓ Use the following equations to find each missing section.
	   ○ Base = Part ÷ Percent
	   ○ Part = Percent × Base
	   ○ Percent = Part ÷ Base

Examples	1) 18 is what percent of 30? **Solution:** In this problem, we are looking for the percent. Use the following equation: $Percent = Part \div Base \rightarrow Percent = 18 \div 30 = 0.6 = 60\%$ 2) 40 is 20% of what number? **Solution:** Use the following formula: $Base = Part \div Percent \rightarrow Base = 40 \div 0.20 = 200$ 40 is 20% of 200.

Your Turn!		
	1) What is 25 percent of 800	2) 26 is what percent of 200? ____
	3) 60 is 5 percent of what number? ____	4) 48 is what percent of 300? ____
	5) 84 is 28 percent of what number? ____	6) 63 is what percent of 700? ____
	7) 96 is 24 percent of what number? ____	8) 40 is what percent of 800? ____

Name: ....

Date: ....

Topic	*Percent of Increase and Decrease*
Notes	✓ Percent of change (increase or decrease) is a mathematical concept that represents the degree of change over time. ✓ To find the percentage of increase or decrease: 1- New Number – Original Number 2- The result ÷ Original Number × 100 Or use this formula: Percent of change = $\frac{new\ number\ -\ original\ number}{original\ number} \times 100$
Example	The price of a printer increases from \$40 to \$50. What is the percent increase? **Solution:** Percent of change = $\frac{new\ number\ -\ original\ number}{original\ number} \times 100 =$ $\frac{50-40}{40} \times 100 = 25$ The percentage increase is 25. It means that the price of the printer increased 25%.
Your Turn!	1) In a class, the number of students has been increased from 32 to 36. What is the percentage increase? _____ % 2) The price of gasoline rose from \$4.50 to \$5.40 in one month. By what percent did the gas price rise? _____ % 3) A shirt was originally priced at \$65.00. It went on sale for \$52.00. What was the percent that the shirt was discounted? _____ % 4) Jason got a raise, and his hourly wage increased from \$40 to \$52. What is the percent increase? _____ %

Name: ....

Date: ....

Topic	*Discount, Tax and Tip*
Notes	✓ Discount = Multiply the regular price by the rate of discount ✓ Selling price = original price – discount ✓ To find tax, multiply the tax rate to the taxable amount (income, property value, etc.) ✓ To find tip, multiply the rate to the selling price.
Example	The original price of a table is $300 and the tax rate is 6%. What is the final price of the table? **Solution:** First find the tax amount. To find tax: Multiply the tax rate to the taxable amount. Tax rate is 6% or 0.06. Then: $0.06 \times 300 = 18$. The tax amount is $18. Final price is: $300 + $18 = $318

Your Turn!	1) Original price of a chair: $300 Tax: 15%, Selling price: $_____	2) Original price of a computer: $750 Discount: 20%, Selling price: $_____
	3) Original price of a printer: $250 Tax: 10%, Selling price: $_____	4) Original price of a sofa: $620 Discount: 25%, Selling price: $_____
	5) Original price of a mattress: $800 Tax: 12%, Selling price: $_____	6) Original price of a book: $150 Discount: 60%, Selling price: $_____
	7) Restaurant bill: $35.00 Tip: 20%, Final amount: $_____	8) Restaurant bill: $60.00 Tip: 25%, Final amount: $_____

Answers– Chapter 5

Percent Problems

1) 200
2) 13%
3) 1200
4) 16%

5) 300
6) 9%
7) 400
8) 5%

Percent of Increase and Decrease

1) 12.5%
2) 20%

3) 20%
4) 30%

Discount, Tax and Tip

1) $345
2) $600
3) $275
4) $465

5) $896
6) $60
7) $42
8) $75

Chapter 6:

Expressions and Variables

Topics that you'll practice in this chapter:

✓ Simplifying Variable Expressions

✓ Simplifying Polynomial Expressions

✓ Evaluating One Variable Expressions

✓ Evaluating Two Variables Expressions

✓ The Distributive Property

Name: ....   **Date:** ....

Topic	*Simplifying Variable Expressions*
Notes	✓ In algebra, a variable is a letter used to stand for a number. The most common letters are: $x, y, z, a, b, c, m, and\ n$. ✓ Algebraic expression is an expression contains integers, variables, and the math operations such as addition, subtraction, multiplication, division, etc. ✓ In an expression, we can combine "like" terms. (values with same variable and same power)
Example	*Simplify this expression.* $(6x + 8x + 9) =?$ **Solution:** Combine like terms. Then: $(6x + 8x + 4) = 14x + 9$ (remember you cannot combine variables and numbers.

Your Turn!	1) $5x + 2 - 2x =$	2) $4 + 7x + 3x =$
	3) $8x + 3 - 3x =$	4) $-2 - x^2 - 6x^2 =$
	5) $3 + 10x^2 + 2 =$	6) $8x^2 + 6x + 7x^2 =$
	7) $5x^2 - 12x^2 + 8x =$	8) $2x^2 - 2x - x + 5x^2 =$
	9) $4x - (12 - 30x) =$	10) $10x - (80x - 48) =$

Name: ....

Date: ....

Topic	*Simplifying Polynomial Expressions*
Notes	✓ In mathematics, a polynomial is an expression consisting of variables and coefficients that involves only the operations of addition, subtraction, multiplication, and non–negative integer exponents of variables. $$P(x) = a_n x^n + a_{n-1} x^{n-1} + \ldots + a_2 x^2 + a_1 x + a_0$$
Example	*Simplify this expression.* $(2x^2 - x^4) - (4x^4 - x^2) =$ **Solution:** First use distributive property: → multiply $(-)$ into $(4x^4 - x^2)$ $(2x^2 - x^4) - (4x^4 - x^2) = 2x^2 - x^4 - 4x^4 + x^2$ Then combine "like" terms: $2x^2 - x^4 - 4x^4 + x^2 = 3x^2 - 5x^4$ And write in standard form: $3x^2 - 5x^4 = -5x^4 + 3x^2$
Your Turn!	1) $(2x^3 + 5x^2) - (12x + 2x^2) =$ 2) $(2x^5 + 2x^3) - (7x^3 + 6x^2) =$ 3) $(12x^4 + 4x^2) - (2x^2 - 6x^4) =$ 4) $14x - 3x^2 - 2(6x^2 + 6x^3) =$ 5) $(5x^3 - 3) + 5(2x^2 - 3x^3) =$ 6) $(4x^3 - 2x) - 2(4x^3 - 2x^4) =$ 7) $2(4x - 3x^3) - 3(3x^3 + 4x^2) =$ 8) $(2x^2 - 2x) - (2x^3 + 5x^2) =$

Name:	Date: ....

Topic	*Evaluating One Variable Expressions*
Notes	✓ To evaluate one variable expression, find the variable and substitute a number for that variable. ✓ Perform the arithmetic operations.
Example	*Find the value of this expression for* $x = -3.$ $-3x - 13$ **Solution:** Substitute -3 for x, then: $-3x - 13 = -3(-3) - 13 = 9 - 13 = -4$

Your Turn!	1) $x = -3 \Rightarrow 3x + 8 =$	2) $x = 4 \Rightarrow 4(2x + 6) =$
	3) $x = -1 \Rightarrow 6x + 4 =$	4) $x = 7 \Rightarrow 6(5x + 3) =$
	5) $x = 4 \Rightarrow 5(3x + 2) =$	6) $x = 6 \Rightarrow 3(2x + 4) =$
	7) $x = 3 \Rightarrow 7(3x + 1) =$	8) $x = 8 \Rightarrow 3(3x + 7) =$
	9) $x = 9 \Rightarrow 2(x + 9) =$	10) $x = 7 \Rightarrow 2(4x + 5) =$

Name: ....

Date: ....

Topic	**Evaluating Two Variables**
Notes	✓ To evaluate an algebraic expression, substitute a number for each variable. ✓ Perform the arithmetic operations to find the value of the expression.
Example	*Evaluate this expression for* $a = 4$ *and* $b = -2$. $5a - 6b$ **Solution:** Substitute 4 for a, and -2 for b , then: $$5a - 6b = 5(4) - 6(-2) = 20 + 12 = 32$$
Your Turn!	1) $-4a + 6b$, $a = 4$, $b = 3$ _____ 2) $5x + 3y$, $x = 2$, $y = -1$ _____ 3) $-5a + 3b$, $a = 2$, $b = -2$ _____ 4) $3x - 4y$, $x = 6$, $y = 2$ _____ 5) $2z + 14 + 6k$, $z = 5$, $k = 3$ _____ 6) $7a - (9 - 3b)$, $a = 1$, $b = 1$ _____ 7) $-6a + 3b$, $a = 4$, $b = 3$ _____ 8) $-2a + b$, $a = 6$, $b = 9$ _____ 9) $8x + 2y$, $x = 4$, $y = 5$ _____ 10) $z + 4 + 2k$, $z = 7$, $k = 4$ _____

| Name: .... | Date: .... |

Topic	*The Distributive Property*
Notes	✓ The distributive property (or the distributive property of multiplication over addition and subtraction) simplifies and solves expressions in the form of: $a(b + c)$ or $a(b - c)$ ✓ Distributive Property rule: $$a(b + c) = ab + ac$$
Example	*Simply.* $(5)(2x - 8)$ **Solution**: Use Distributive Property rule: $a(b + c) = ab + ac$ $(5)(2x - 8) = (5 \times 2x) + (5) \times (-8) = 10x - 40$

Your Turn!	1) $(-2)(4 - 3x) =$	2) $(6 - 3x)(-7)$
	3) $6\,(5 - 9x) =$	4) $10(3 - 5x) =$
	5) $5(6 - 5x) =$	6) $(-2)(-5x + 3) =$
	7) $(8 - 9x)(5) =$	8) $(-16x + 15)(-3) =$
	9) $(-2x + 7)(3) =$	10) $(-18x + 25)(-2) =$

Answers– Chapter 6

Simplifying Variable Expressions

1) $3x + 2$
2) $10x + 4$
3) $5x + 3$
4) $-7x^2 - 2$
5) $10x^2 + 5$

6) $15x^2 + 6x$
7) $-7x^2 + 8x$
8) $72x^2 - 3x$
9) $34x - 12$
10) $-70x - 48$

Simplifying Polynomial Expressions

1) $2x^3 + 3x^2 - 12x$
2) $2x^5 - 5x^3 - 6x^2$
3) $18x^4 + 2x^2$
4) $-12x^3 - 15x^2 + 14x$

5) $-10x^3 + 10x^2 - 3$
6) $4x^4 - 4x^3 - 2$
7) $-15x^3 - 12x^2 + 8x$
8) $2x^3 - 3x^2 - 2x$

Evaluating One Variables

1) -1
2) 56
3) -2
4) 228
5) 70

6) 48
7) 70
8) 93
9) 36
10) 66

Evaluating Two Variables

1) 2
2) 7
3) -16
4) 10
5) 42

6) 1
7) -15
8) -3
9) 42
10) 1

The Distributive Property

1) $6x - 8$
2) $21x - 42$
3) $-54x + 30$
4) $-50x + 30$
5) $-25x + 30$

6) $10x - 6$
7) $-45x + 40$
8) $48x - 45$
9) $-6x + 21$
10) $36x - 50$

Chapter 7:

Equations and Inequalities

Topics that you'll practice in this chapter:

✓ One–Step Equations

✓ Multi–Step Equations

✓ System of Equations

✓ Graphing Single–Variable Inequalities

✓ One–Step Inequalities

✓ Multi-Step Inequalities

Name: .... **Date:** ....

Topic	*One–Step Equations*

Notes	✓ You only need to perform one Math operation in order to solve the one-step equations.
	✓ To solve one-step equation, find the inverse (opposite) operation is being performed.
	✓ The inverse operations are:
	   - Addition and subtraction
	   - Multiplication and division

Example	*Solve this equation.* $x + 42 = 60 \Rightarrow x = ?$ **Solution:** Here, the operation is addition and its inverse operation is subtraction. To solve this equation, subtract 42 from both sides of the equation: $x + 42 - 42 = 60 - 42$ Then simplify: $x + 42 - 42 = 60 - 42 \Rightarrow x = 18$
Your Turn!	1) $x - 15 = 36 \Rightarrow x =$ ____ 2) $18 = 13 + x \Rightarrow x =$ ____ 3) $x - 22 = 54 \Rightarrow x =$ ____ 4) $x + 14 = 24 \Rightarrow x =$ ___ 5) $4x = 24 \Rightarrow x =$ ___ 6) $\frac{x}{6} = -3 \Rightarrow x =$ ___ 7) $99 = 11x \Rightarrow x =$ ___ 8) $\frac{x}{12} = 6 \Rightarrow x =$ ___

Name: ....

Date: ....

Topic	***Multi –Step Equations***
Notes	✓ Combine "like" terms on one side. ✓ Bring variables to one side by adding or subtracting. ✓ Simplify using the inverse of addition or subtraction. ✓ Simplify further by using the inverse of multiplication or division. ✓ Check your solution by plugging the value of the variable into the original equation.
Example	*Solve this equation for* x. $2x - 3 = 13$ **Solution:** The inverse of subtraction is addition. Add 3 to both sides of the equation. Then: $2x - 3 = 13 \Rightarrow 2x - 3 = 13 + 3$ $\Rightarrow 2x = 16$. **Now, divide** both sides by 2, then: $\frac{2x}{2} = \frac{16}{2} \Rightarrow x = 8$ Now, check the solution: $x = 8 \Rightarrow 2x - 3 = 13 \Rightarrow 2(8) - 3 = 13 \Rightarrow 16 - 3 = 13$ The answer $x = 8$ is correct.
Your Turn!	1) $4x - 12 = 8 \Rightarrow x =$ 2) $12 - 3x = -6 + 3x \Rightarrow x =$ 3) $3(4 - 2x) = 24 \Rightarrow x =$ 4) $15 + 5x = -7 - 6x \Rightarrow x =$ 5) $-2(5 + x) = 2 \Rightarrow x$ 6) $12 - 2x = -3 - 5x \Rightarrow x =$ 7) $14 = -(x - 9) \Rightarrow x =$ 8) $11 - 4x = -4 - 3x \Rightarrow x =$

Name: ....

Date: ....

Topic	*System of Equations*
Notes	✓ A system of equations contains two equations and two variables. For example, consider the system of equations: $x - 2y = -2, x + 2y = 10$ ✓ The easiest way to solve a system of equation is using the elimination method. The elimination method uses the addition property of equality. You can add the same value to each side of an equation. ✓ For the first equation above, you can add $x + 2y$ to the left side and 10 to the right side of the first equation: $x - 2y + (x + 2y) = -2 + 10$. Now, if you simplify, you get: $x - 2y + (x + 2y) = -2 + 10 \rightarrow 2x = 8 \rightarrow x = 4$. Now, substitute 4 for the x in the first equation: $4 - 2y = -2$. By solving this equation, $y = 3$
Example	What is the value of x and y in this system of equations? $\begin{cases} 3x - y = 7 \\ -x + 4y = 5 \end{cases}$ **Solution:** Solving System of Equations by Elimination: $\begin{array}{c} 3x - y = 7 \\ \underline{-x + 4y = 5} \end{array}$ Multiply the second equation by 3, then add it to the first equation. $\begin{array}{c} 3x - y = 7 \\ 3(-x + 4y = 5) \end{array} \Rightarrow \begin{array}{c} 3x - y = 7 \\ \underline{-3x + 12y = 15)} \end{array} \Rightarrow 11y = 22 \Rightarrow y = 2.$ Now, substitute 2 for y in the first equation and solve for x. $3x - (2) = 7 \Rightarrow 3x = 9 \Rightarrow x = 3$
Your Turn!	

1) $-4x + 4y = 8$
   $-4x + 2y = 6$
	2) $-5x + y = -3$
	   $3x - 8y = 24$

$x = $ _____ , $y = $ _____	$x = $ _____ , $y = $ _____

3) $y = -2$
   $4x - 3y = 8$
	4) $y = -3x + 5$
	   $5x - 4y = -3$

$x = $ _____ , $y = $ _____	$x = $ _____ , $y = $ _____

5) $20x - 18y = -26$
   $-10x + 6y = 22$
	6) $-9x - 12y = 15$
	   $2x - 6y = 14$

$x = $ _____ , $y = $ _____	$x = $ _____ , $y = $ _____

Name: .... Date: ....

Topic	*Graphing Single–Variable Inequalities*
Notes	✓ An inequality compares two expressions using an inequality sign. ✓ Inequality signs are: "less than" $<$, "greater than" $>$, "less than or equal to" $\leq$, and "greater than or equal to" $\geq$. ✓ To graph a single–variable inequality, find the value of the inequality on the number line. ✓ For less than ($<$) or greater than ($>$) draw open circle on the value of the variable. If there is an equal sign too, then use filled circle. ✓ Draw an arrow to the right for greater or to the left for less than.
Example	*Draw a graph for this inequality.* $x < 5$ **Solution:** Since, the variable is less than 5, then we need to find 5 in the number line and draw an open circle on it. Then, draw an arrow to the left.

Your Turn!	1) $x < 4$	2) $x \geq -1$
	3) $x \geq -3$	4) $x \leq 6$
	5) $x > -6$	6) $2 > x$
	7) $-2 \leq x$	8) $x > 0$

Name: ....

Date: ....

Topic	*One–Step Inequalities*
Notes	✓ Inequality signs are: "less than" <, "greater than" >, "less than or equal to" ≤, and "greater than or equal to" ≥. ✓ You only need to perform one Math operation in order to solve the one-step inequalities. ✓ To solve one-step inequalities, find the inverse (opposite) operation is being performed. ✓ For dividing or multiplying both sides by negative numbers, flip the direction of the inequality sign.
Example	*Solve this inequality.* $x + 12 < 60 \Rightarrow$ _____ **Solution:** Here, the operation is addition and its inverse operation is subtraction. To solve this inequality, subtract 12 from both sides of the *inequality:* $x + 12 - 12 < 60 - 12$ Then simplify: $x < 48$
Your Turn!	1) $4x < -8 \Rightarrow$ _____ 2) $x + 6 > 28 \Rightarrow$ _____ 3) $-3x \geq 36 \Rightarrow$ _____ 4) $x - 16 \leq 4 \Rightarrow$ _____ 5) $\frac{x}{2} \geq -9 \Rightarrow$ _____ 6) $48 < 6x \Rightarrow$ _____ 7) $77 \leq 11x \Rightarrow$ _____ 8) $\frac{x}{4} > 9 \Rightarrow$ _____

| Name: .... | Date: .... |

Topic	**Multi –Step Inequalities**
Notes	✓ Isolate the variable. ✓ Simplify using the inverse of addition or subtraction. ✓ Simplify further by using the inverse of multiplication or division. ✓ For dividing or multiplying both sides by negative numbers, flip the direction of the inequality sign.
Example	*Solve this inequality.* $3x + 12 \leq 21$ **Solution:** First subtract 12 from both sides: $3x + 12 - 12 \leq 21 - 12$ Then simplify: $3x + 12 - 12 \leq 21 - 12 \rightarrow 3x \leq 9$ Now divide both sides by 3: $\frac{3x}{3} \leq \frac{9}{3} \rightarrow x \leq 3$
Your Turn!	1) $5x + 6 < 36 \rightarrow$ _____ 2) $2x - 8 \leq 6 \rightarrow$ _____ 3) $2x - 5 \leq 17 \rightarrow$ _____ 4) $14 - 7x \geq -7 \rightarrow$ _____ 5) $18 - 6x \geq -6 \rightarrow$ _____ 6) $2x - 18 \leq 16 \rightarrow$ _____ 7) $8 + 4x < 44 \rightarrow$ _____ 8) $5 - 4x < 17 \rightarrow$ _____

Answers– Chapter 7

One–Step Equations

1) 51
2) 5
3) 76
4) 10

5) 6
6) −18
7) 9
8) 72

Multi–Step Equations

1) 5
2) 3
3) −2
4) −2

5) −6
6) −5
7) −5
8) 15

System of Equations

1) $x = -1,, y = 1$
2) $x = 0, y = -3$
3) $x = \frac{1}{2}, y = -2$

4) $x = 1, y = 2$
5) $x = -4, y = -3$
6) $x = 1, y = -2$

Graphing Single–Variable Inequalities

1) $x < 4$

2) $x \geq -1$

3) $x \geq -3$

4) $x \leq 6$

5) $x > -6$

6) $2 > x$

7) $-2 \leq x$

8) $x > 0$

One–Step Inequalities

1) $x < -2$
2) $x > 22$
3) $x \leq -12$
4) $x \leq 20$

5) $x \geq -18$
6) $8 < x$
7) $7 \leq x$
8) $x > 36$

Multi-Step Inequalities

1) $x < 6$
2) $x \leq 7$
3) $x \leq 11$
4) $x \leq 3$

5) $x \leq 4$
6) $x \leq 17$
7) $x < 9$
8) $x > -3$

Chapter 8:

Line and Slope

Topics that you'll practice in this chapter:

- ✓ Finding Slope
- ✓ Graphing Lines Using Line Equation
- ✓ Writing Linear Equations
- ✓ Graphing Linear Inequalities
- ✓ Finding Midpoint
- ✓ Finding Distance of Two Points

Name: ....

Date: ....

Topic	*Finding Slope*
Notes	✓ The slope of a line represents the direction of a line on the coordinate plane. ✓ A line on coordinate plane can be drawn by connecting two points. ✓ To find the slope of a line, we need two points. ✓ The slope of a line with two points A (x_1, y_1) and B (x_2, y_2) can be found by using this formula: $\frac{y_2 - y_1}{x_2 - x_1} = \frac{rise}{run}$ ✓ The equation of a line is typically written as $y = mx + b$ where m is the slope and b is the y-intercept.
Examples	1) *Find the slope of the line through these two points*: $(4, -12)$ *and* $(9, 8)$. **Solution:** Slope $= \frac{y_2 - y_1}{x_2 - x_1}$. Let (x_1, y_1) be $(4, -12)$ and (x_2, y_2) be $(9, 8)$. ***Then:*** slope $= \frac{y_2 - y_1}{x_2 - x_1} = \frac{8 - (-12)}{9 - 4} = \frac{8 + 1}{5} = \frac{20}{5} = 4$ 2) *Find the slope of the line with equation* $y = 5x - 6$ **Solution:** when the equation of a line is written in the form of $y = mx + b$, the slope is m. In this line: $y = 5x - 6$, the slope is 5.
Your Turn!	1) $(2, 3), (4, 7)$ Slope = ____ | 2) $(-2, 2), (0, 4)$ Slope = ____ 3) $(4, -2), (2, 4)$ Slope = ____ | 4) $(-4, -1), (0, 7)$ Slope = ____ 5) $y = 3x + 18$ Slope = ____ | 6) $y = 12x - 3$ Slope = ____

Name: ....

Date: ....

Topic	*Graphing Lines Using Slope–Intercept Form*
Notes	✓ Slope–intercept form of a line: given the slope m and the y–intercept (the intersection of the line and y-axis) b, then the equation of the line is: $$y = mx + b$$
Example	*Sketch the graph of $y = -2x - 1$.* **Solution:** To graph this line, we need to find two points. When x is zero the value of y is -1. And when y is zero the value of x is $-\frac{1}{2}$. $$x = 0 \rightarrow y = -2(0) - 1 = -1, y = 0 \rightarrow 0$$ $$= -2x - 1 \rightarrow x = -\frac{1}{2}$$ Now, we have two points: $(0, -1)$ and $(-\frac{1}{2}, 0)$. Find the points and graph the line. Remember that the slope of the line is $-\frac{1}{2}$.
Your Turn!	1) $y = -4x + 1$ 2) $y = -x - 5$

Name:	Date: ....

Topic	*Writing Linear Equations*	
Notes	✓ The equation of a line: $y = mx + b$ ✓ Identify the slope. ✓ Find the y–intercept. This can be done by substituting the slope and the coordinates of a point (x, y) on the line.	
Example	*Write the equation of the line through* $(3, 1)$ *and* $(-1, 5)$. **Solution:** $Slop = \frac{y_2 - y_1}{x_2 - x_1} = \frac{5 - 1}{-1 - 3} = \frac{4}{-4} = -1 \rightarrow m = -1$ To find the value of b, you can use either points. The answer will be the same: $y = -x + b$ $(3, 1) \rightarrow 1 = -3 + b \rightarrow b = 4$ $(-1, 5) \rightarrow 5 = -(-1) + b \rightarrow b = 4$ The equation of the line is: $y = -x + 4$	
Your Turn!	1) through: $(-2, 7), (1, 4)$ $y =$	2) through: $(6, 1), (5, 2)$ $y =$
	3) through: $(5, -1), (8, 2)$ $y =$	4) through: $(-2, 4), (4, -8)$ $y =$
	5) through: $(6, -5), (-5, 6)$ $y =$	6) through: $(4, -4), (-2, 8)$ $y =$
	7) through $(8, 8)$, Slope: 2 $y =$	8) through $(-7, 10)$, Slope: -2 $y =$

Name: ....

Date: ....

Topic	*Finding Midpoint*
Notes	✓ The middle of a line segment is its midpoint. ✓ The Midpoint of two endpoints A (x_1, y_1) and B (x_2, y_2) can be found using this formula: $M(\frac{x_1+x_2}{2}, \frac{y_1+y_2}{2})$
Example	Find the midpoint of the line segment with the given endpoints. $(1, -2), (3, 6)$ **Solution:** Midpoint $= (\frac{x_1+x_2}{2}, \frac{y_1+y_2}{2}) \rightarrow (x_1, y_1) = (1, -2)$ and $(x_2, y_2) = (3, 6)$ Midpoint $= (\frac{1+3}{2}, \frac{-2+6}{2}) \rightarrow (\frac{4}{2}, \frac{4}{2}) \rightarrow M(2, 2)$

Your Turn!	1) $(6, 0), (-4, 2)$ Midpoint $= (\_\_, \_\_)$	2) $(4, -1), (2, 3)$ Midpoint $= (\_\_, \_\_)$
	3) $(-3, 4), (-5, 0)$ Midpoint $= (\_\_, \_\_)$	4) $(8, 1), (-4, 5)$ Midpoint $= (\_\_, \_\_)$
	5) $(6, 7), (-4, 5)$ Midpoint $= (\_\_, \_\_)$	6) $(2, -3), (2, 5)$ Midpoint $= (\_\_, \_\_)$
	7) $(7, 3), (-1, -7)$ Midpoint $= (\_\_, \_\_)$	8) $(3, 9), (-1, 5)$ Midpoint $= (\_\_, \_\_)$
	9) $(3, 4), (-7, -6)$ Midpoint $= (\_\_, \_\_)$	10) $(-5, 2), (11, -6)$ Midpoint $= (\_\_, \_\_)$

Name:	Date: ....

Topic	**_Finding Distance of Two Points_**
Notes	✓ Use this formula to find the distance of two points A (x_1, y_1) and B (x_2, y_2): $d = \sqrt{(x_2 - x_1)^2 + (y_2 - y_1)^2}$
Example	Find the distance of two points $(-1, 5)$ *and* $(4, -7)$. **Solution: _Use distance of two points formula:_** $d = \sqrt{(x_2 - x_1)^2 + (y_2 - y_1)^2}$ $(x_1, y_1) = (-1, 5)$, and $(x_2, y_2) = (4, -7)$ Then: $d = \sqrt{(x_2 - x_1)^2 + (y_2 - y_1)^2} \rightarrow d = \sqrt{(4 - (-1))^2 + (-7 - 5)^2} = \sqrt{(-5)^2 + (-12)^2} = \sqrt{25 + 144} = \sqrt{169} = 13$
Your Turn!	1) $(6, 2), (-4, 2)$ **_Distance_ = ____** 2) $(2, -3), (2, 5)$ **_Distance_ = ____** 3) $(-5, 10), (7, 1)$ **_Distance_ = ____** 4) $(8, 1), (-4, 6)$ **_Distance_ = ____** 5) $(-3, 6), (-4, 5)$ **_Distance_ = ____** 6) $(4, -1), (14, 23)$ **_Distance_ = ____** 7) $(-3, 4), (-5, 0)$ **_Distance_ = ____** 8) $(3, 9), (-1, 5)$ **_Distance_ = ____**

Answers– Chapter 8

Finding Slope

1) 2
2) 1
3) −3

4) 2
5) 3
6) 12

Graphing Lines Using Line Equation

1) $y = -4x + 1$

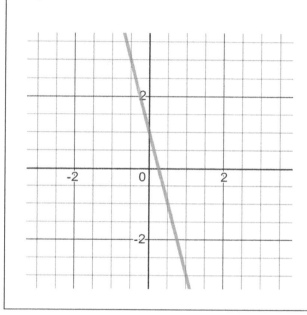

2) $y = -x - 5$

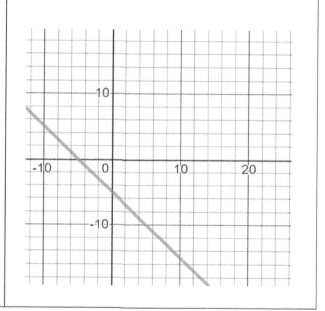

Writing Linear Equations

1) $y = -x + 5$
2) $y = -x + 7$
3) $y = x - 6$
4) $y = -2x$

5) $y = -x + 1$
6) $y = -2x + 4$
7) $y = 2x - 8$
8) $y = -2x - 4$

Finding Midpoint

1) $(1, 1)$
2) $(3, 1)$
3) $(-4, 2)$
4) $(2, 3)$
5) $(1, 6)$

6) $(2, 1)$
7) $(3, -2)$
8) $(1, 7)$
9) $(-2, -1)$
10) $(3, -2)$

Finding Distance of Two Points

1) 10
2) 8
3) 15
4) 13

5) $\sqrt{2}$
6) 26
7) $\sqrt{20} = 2\sqrt{5}$
8) $\sqrt{32} = 4\sqrt{2}$

Chapter 9:

Exponents and Variables

Topics that you'll practice in this chapter:

- ✓ Multiplication Property of Exponents
- ✓ Zero and Negative Exponents
- ✓ Division Property of Exponents
- ✓ Powers of Products and Quotients
- ✓ Negative Exponents and Negative Bases
- ✓ Scientific Notation
- ✓ Radicals

| Name: .... | Date: .... |

Topic	**Multiplication Property of Exponents**
Notes	✓ Exponents are shorthand for repeated multiplication of the same number by itself. For example, instead of 2×2, we can write 2^2. For $3 \times 3 \times 3 \times 3$, we can write 3^4 ✓ In algebra, a variable is a letter used to stand for a number. The most common letters are: $x, y, z, a, b, c, m,$ and n. ✓ Exponent's rules: $x^a \times x^b = x^{a+b}$, $\dfrac{x^a}{x^b} = x^{a-b}$ $\quad (x^a)^b = x^{a \times b} \qquad\qquad (xy)^a = x^a \times y^a \qquad (\frac{a}{b})^c = \dfrac{a^c}{b^c}$
Example	*Multiply.* $4x^3 \times 2x^2$ **Solution:** Use Exponent's rules: $x^a \times x^b = x^{a+b} \rightarrow x^3 \times x^2 = x^{3+2} = x^5$ Then: $4x^3 \times 2x^2 = 8x^5$
Your Turn!	1) $x^2 \times 3x =$ 2) $5x^4 \times x^2 =$ 3) $3x^2 \times 4x^5 =$ 4) $3x^2 \times 6xy =$ 5) $3x^5y \times 5x^2y^3 =$ 6) $3x^2y^2 \times 5x^2y^8 =$ 7) $5x^2y \times 5x^2y^7 =$ 8) $6x^6 \times 4x^9y^4 =$ 9) $8x^2y^5 \times 7x^5y^3 =$ 10) $12x^6x^2 \times 3xy^5 =$

| Name: .... | Date: .... |

Topic	**Zero and Negative Exponents**
Notes	✓ A negative exponent is the reciprocal of that number with a positive exponent. $(3)^{-2} = \frac{1}{3^2}$ ✓ Zero-Exponent Rule: $a^0 = 1$, this means that anything raised to the zero power is 1. For example: $(28x^2y)^0 = 1$
Example	*Evaluate.* $\left(\frac{1}{3}\right)^{-2} =$ **Solution:** Use negative exponent's rule: $\left(\frac{1}{x^a}\right)^{-2} = (x^a)^2 \to \left(\frac{1}{3}\right)^{-2} = (3)^2 =$ Then: $(3)^2 = 9$

Your Turn!	1) $2^{-3} =$	2) $3^{-3} =$
	3) $7^{-3} =$	4) $1^{-3} =$
	5) $8^{-3} =$	6) $4^{-4} =$
	7) $10^{-3} =$	8) $7^{-4} =$
	9) $\left(\frac{1}{8}\right)^{-1} =$	10) $\left(\frac{1}{5}\right)^{-2} =$

Name:	Date: ....

Topic	*Division Property of Exponents*	
Notes	✓ For division of exponents use these formulas: $\frac{x^a}{x^b} = x^{a-b}$, $x \neq 0$ $$\frac{x^a}{x^b} = \frac{1}{x^{b-a}}, x \neq 0, \qquad \frac{1}{x^b} = x^{-b}$$	
Example	*Simplify.* $\frac{6x^3y}{36x^2y^3}$ **Solution:** First cancel the common factor: $6 \rightarrow \frac{6x^3y}{36x^2y^3} = \frac{x^3y}{6x^2y^3}$ Use Exponent's rules: $\frac{x^a}{x^b} = x^{a-b} \rightarrow \frac{x^3}{x^2} = x^{3-2} = x^1 = x$ Then: $\frac{6x^3y}{36x^2y^3} = \frac{xy}{9y^3} \rightarrow$ now cancel the common factor: $y \rightarrow \frac{xy}{6y^3} = \frac{x}{6y^2}$	
Your Turn!	1) $\dfrac{3^7}{3^2} =$	2) $\dfrac{5x}{10x^3} =$
	3) $\dfrac{3x^3}{2x^5} =$	4) $\dfrac{12x^3}{14x^6} =$
	5) $\dfrac{12x^3}{9y^8} =$	6) $\dfrac{25xy^4}{5x^6y^2} =$
	7) $\dfrac{2x^4y^5}{7xy^2} =$	8) $\dfrac{16x^2y^8}{4x^3} =$
	9) $\dfrac{12x^4}{15x^7y^9} =$	10) $\dfrac{12yx^4}{10yx^8} =$

Name:	Date: ....

Topic	***Powers of Products and Quotients***
Notes	For any nonzero numbers a and b and any integer x, $$(ab)^x = a^x \times b^x, (\frac{a}{b})^c = \frac{a^c}{b^c}$$
Example	*Simplify.* $\left(\frac{2x^3}{x}\right)^2$ **Solution:** First cancel the common factor: $x \rightarrow \left(\frac{2x^3}{x}\right)^2 = (2x^2)^2$ Use Exponent's rules: $(ab)^x = a^x \times b^x$ Then: $(2x^2)^2 = (2)^2(x^2)^2 = 4x^4$

Your Turn!	1) $(4x^3x^3)^2 =$	2) $(3x^3 \times 5x)^2 =$
	3) $(10x^{11}y^3)^2 =$	4) $(9x^7y^5)^2 =$
	5) $(4x^4y^6)^3 =$	6) $(3x \times 4y^3)^2 =$
	7) $(\frac{5x}{x^2})^2 =$	8) $\left(\frac{x^4y^4}{x^2y^2}\right)^3 =$
	9) $\left(\frac{25x}{5x^6}\right)^2 =$	10) $\left(\frac{x^8}{x^6y^2}\right)^2 =$

Name:	Date: ....

Topic	*Negative Exponents and Negative Bases*
Notes	✓ Make the power positive. A negative exponent is the reciprocal of that number with a positive exponent. ✓ The parenthesis is important! $\mathbf{5^{-2}}$ is not the same as $(-\ \mathbf{5})^{-2}$ $(-\ 5)^{-2} = -\dfrac{1}{5^2}$ and $(-5)^{-2} = +\dfrac{1}{5^2}$
Example	*Simplify.* $\left(-\dfrac{3x}{4yz}\right)^{-2} =$ **Solution:** Use negative exponent's rule: $\left(\dfrac{x^a}{x^b}\right)^{-2} = \left(\dfrac{x^b}{x^a}\right)^2 \rightarrow \left(-\dfrac{3x}{4y}\right)^{-3} = \left(-\dfrac{4yz}{3x}\right)^3$ Now use exponent's rule: $\left(\dfrac{a}{b}\right)^c = \dfrac{a^c}{b^c} \rightarrow \left(-\dfrac{4yz}{3x}\right)^3 = \dfrac{4^3 y^3 z^3}{3^3 x^3} = \dfrac{64 y^3 z^3}{27 x^3}$
Your Turn!	1) $-5x^{-2}y^{-3} =$ 2) $20x^{-4}y^{-1} =$ 3) $14a^{-6}b^{-7} =$ 4) $-12x^2y^{-3} =$ 5) $-\dfrac{25}{x^{-6}} =$ 6) $\dfrac{7b}{-9c^{-4}} =$ 7) $\dfrac{7ab}{a^{-3}b^{-1}} =$ 8) $-\dfrac{5n^{-2}}{10p^{-3}} = -$ 9) $\dfrac{4ab^{-2}}{-3c^{-2}} =$ 10) $\left(\dfrac{3a}{2c}\right)^{-2} =$

Name: .... Date: ....

Topic	*Scientific Notation*
Notes	✓ It is used to write very big or very small numbers in decimal form. ✓ In scientific notation all numbers are written in the form of: $$m \times 10^n$$ **Decimal notation** **Scientific notation** 3 3×10^0 $-45{,}000$ -4.5×10^4 0.3 3×10^{-1} $2{,}122.456$ 2.122456×10^3
Example	*Write* 0.00054 *in scientific notation.* **Solution:** First, move the decimal point to the right so that you have a number that is between 1 and 10. Then: $m = 5.4$ Now, determine how many places the decimal moved in step 1 by the power of 10. Then: 10^{-4} → When the decimal moved to the right, the exponent is negative. Then: $0.00054 = 5.4 \times 10^{-4}$
Your Turn!	1) $0.000325 =$ 2) $0.000023 =$ 3) $52{,}000{,}000 =$ 4) $21{,}000 =$ 5) $3 \times 10^{-1} =$ 6) $5 \times 10^{-2} =$ 7) $1.2 \times 10^3 =$ 8) $2 \times 10^{-4} =$

Answers– Chapter 9

Multiplication Property of Exponents

1) $3x^3$
2) $5x^6$
3) $12x^7$
4) $18x^3y$
5) $15x^7y^4$

6) $15x^4y^{10}$
7) $25x^4y^8$
8) $24x^{15}y^4$
9) $56x^7y^8$
10) $36x^9y^5$

Zero and Negative Exponents

1) $\frac{1}{8}$
2) $\frac{1}{27}$
3) $\frac{1}{343}$
4) 1
5) $\frac{1}{512}$

6) $\frac{1}{256}$
7) $\frac{1}{1,000}$
8) $\frac{1}{2,401}$
9) 8
10) 25

Division Property of Exponents

1) 3^5
2) $\frac{1}{2x^2}$
3) $\frac{3}{2x^2}$
4) $\frac{6}{7x^3}$
5) $\frac{4x^3}{3y^8}$

6) $\frac{5y^2}{x^5}$
7) $\frac{2x^3y^3}{7}$
8) $\frac{4y^8}{x}$
9) $\frac{4}{5x^3y^9}$
10) $\frac{6y^6}{5x^4}$

Powers of Products and Quotients

1) $16x^{12}$
2) $225x^8$
3) $100x^{22}y^6$
4) $81x^{14}y^{10}$
5) $64\,x^{12}y^{18}$
6) $144x^2y^6$

7) $\frac{25}{x^2}$
8) x^6y^6
9) $\frac{25}{x^{10}}$
10) $\frac{x^4}{y^4}$

Negative Exponents and Negative Bases

1) $-\dfrac{5}{x^2 y^3}$

2) $\dfrac{20}{x^4 y}$

3) $\dfrac{14}{a^6 b^7}$

4) $-\dfrac{12x^2}{y^3}$

5) $-25x^6$

6) $-\dfrac{7bc^4}{9}$

7) $7a^4 b^2$

8) $-\dfrac{p^3}{2n^2}$

9) $-\dfrac{4ac^2}{3b^2}$

10) $\dfrac{4c^2}{9a^2}$

Scientific Notation

1) 3.25×10^{-4}

2) 2.3×10^{-5}

3) 5.2×10^7

4) 2.1×10^4

5) 0.3

6) 0.05

7) $1,200$

8) 0.0002

Chapter 10:

Polynomials

Topics that you'll practice in this chapter:

✓ Simplifying Polynomials

✓ Adding and Subtracting Polynomials

✓ Multiplying Monomials

✓ Multiplying and Dividing Monomials

✓ Multiplying a Polynomial and a Monomial

✓ Multiplying Binomials

✓ Factoring Trinomials

Name: ....

Date: ....

Topic	*Simplifying Polynomials*
Notes	✓ Find "like" terms. (they have same variables with same power). ✓ Use "FOIL". (First–Out–In–Last) for binomials: $$(x + a)(x + b) = x^2 + (b + a)x + ab$$ ✓ Add or Subtract "like" terms using order of operation.
Example	*Simplify this expression.* $(x + 3)(x - 8) =$ **Solution:** First apply FOIL method: $(a + b)(c + d) = ac + ad + bc + bd$ $(x + 3)(x - 8) = x^2 - 8x + 3x - 24$ Now combine like terms: $x^2 - 8x + 3x - 24 = x^2 - 5x - 24$
Your Turn!	1) $-(2x - 4) =$ _____ 2) $2(2x + 6) =$ _____ 3) $3x(3x - 4) =$ _____ 4) $5x(2x + 8) =$ _____ 5) $-2x(5x + 6) + 5x =$ _____ 6) $-4x(8x - 3) - x^2 =$ _____ 7) $(x + 4)(x + 5) =$ _____ 8) $(x + 2)(x + 8) =$ _____ 9) $-4x^2 + 10x^3 + 5x^2 =$ _____ 10) $-3x^5 + 10x^4 + 5x^5 =$ _____

| Name: .... | Date: .... |

Topic	**Adding and Subtracting Polynomials**	
Notes	✓ Adding polynomials is just a matter of combining like terms, with some order of operations considerations thrown in. ✓ Be careful with the minus signs, and don't confuse addition and multiplication!	
Example	*Simplify the expressions.* $(3x^2 - 4x^3) - (5x^3 - 8x^2) =$ **Solution:** First use Distributive Property: $-(5x^3 - 8x^2) = -5x^3 + 8x^2$ $\rightarrow (3x^2 - 4x^3) - (5x^3 - 8x^2) = 3x^2 - 4x^3 - 5x^3 + 8x^2$ Now combine like terms: $3x^2 - 4x^3 - 5x^3 + 8x^2 = -9x^3 + 11x^2$	
Your Turn!	1) $(x^2 - x) + (4x^2 - 5) =$ _____	2) $(2x^3 + x) - (x^3 + 2) =$ _____
	3) $(x^2 - 5x) + (6x^2 - 5) =$ _____	4) $(8x^2 - 2) - (3x^2 + 7) =$ _____
	5) $(3x^2 + 2) - (2 - 4x^2) =$ _____	6) $(x^3 + x^2) - (x^3 - 10) =$ _____
	7) $(3x^3 - 2x) - (x - x^3) =$ _____	8) $(x - 5x^4) - (2x^4 + 3x) =$ _____
	9) $(6x^3 + 5) - (4 - 5x^3) =$ _____	10) $(2x^2 + 5x^3) - (6x^3 + 7) =$ _____

Name: ....   Date: ....

Topic	**Multiplying Monomials**
Notes	✓ A monomial is a polynomial with just one term: Examples: $5x$ or $7x^2yz^8$. ✓ When you multiply monomials, first multiply the coefficients (a number placed before and multiplying the variable) and then multiply the variables using multiplication property of exponents. $x^a \times x^b = x^{a+b}$
Example	*Multiply.* $(-3xy^4z^5) \times (2x^2y^5z^3) =$ **Solution:** Multiply coefficients and find same variables and use multiplication property of exponents: $x^a \times x^b = x^{a+b}$ $-3 \times 2 = -6$, $x \times x^2 = x^{1+2} = x^3$, $y^4 \times y^5 = y^{4+5} = y^9$, and $z^2 \times z^5 = z^{2+5} = z^7$ Then: $(-3xy^4z^5) \times (2x^2y^5z^3) = -6x^3y^9z^7$
Your Turn!	1) $2x^2 \times 4x^6 =$ 2) $5x^7 \times 6x^4 =$ 3) $-2x^2y^4 \times 6x^3y^2 =$ 4) $-5x^5y \times 3x^3y^4 =$ 5) $8x^7y^5 \times 5x^6y^3 =$ 6) $-6x^7y^5 \times (-3x^9y^8) =$ 7) $12x^8y^8z^4 \times 3x^4y^3z =$ 8) $-8x^9y^7z^{11} \times 7x^6y^7z^5 =$

Name:	Date: ....

Topic	*Multiplying and Dividing Monomials*	
Notes	✓ When you divide or multiply two monomials you need to divide or multiply their coefficients and then divide or multiply their variables. ✓ In case of exponents with the same base, you need to subtract their powers. ✓ Exponent's rules: $$x^a \times x^b = x^{a+b}, \qquad \frac{x^a}{x^b} = x^{a-b}$$ $$\frac{1}{x^b} = x^{-b}, \quad (x^a)^b = x^{a \times b}$$ $$(xy)^a = x^a \times y^a$$	
Example	*Divide expressions.* $\frac{-18x^5y^6}{2xy^2} =$ **Solution:** Use exponents' division rule: $\frac{x^a}{x^b} = x^{a-b}, \frac{x^5}{x} = x^{5-1} = x^4$ and $\frac{y^6}{y^2} = y^4$ Then: $\frac{-18x^5y^6}{2xy^2} = -9x^4y^4$	
Your Turn!	1) $(x^8y)(xy^2) =$ ——— 3) $(x^7y^4)(2x^5y^2) =$ ——— 5) $(-6x^8y^7)(4x^6y^9) =$ ——— 7) $\frac{30x^8y^9}{6x^5y^4} =$ ———	2) $(x^4y^3)(x^2y^3) =$ ——— 4) $(3x^5y^4)(4x^6y^3) =$ ——— 6) $(-2x^9y^3)(9x^7y^8) =$ ——— 8) $\frac{-42x^{12}y^{16}}{7x^8y^9} =$ ———

Name: ....

Date: ....

Topic	*Multiplying a Polynomial and a Monomial*
Notes	✓ When multiplying monomials, use the product rule for exponents. $$x^a \times x^b = x^{a+b}$$ ✓ When multiplying a monomial by a polynomial, use the distributive property. $$a \times (b + c) = a \times b + a \times c = ab + ac$$ $$a \times (b - c) = a \times b - a \times c = ab - ac$$
Example	*Multiply expressions.* $4x(5x - 8) =$ **Solution:** Use Distributive Property: $4x(5x - 8) = 4x \times 5x - 4x \times (8) =$ Now, simplify: $4x \times 5x - 4x \times (8) = 20x^2 - 32x$
Your Turn!	1) $3x(2x + y) = $ _____ 2) $x(x - 3y) = $ _____ 3) $-x(5x - 3y) = $ ___ _____ 4) $4x(x + 5y) = $ ___ _____ 5) $-x(5x + 8y) = $ ___ _____ 6) $2x(6x - 7y) = $ ___ _____ 7) $-3x(x^3 + 4y^2 - 6x) = $ ___ 8) $7x(x^2 - 5y^2 + 4) = $ ___

Name:	Date: ....

Topic	**Multiplying Binomials**
Notes	✓ A binomial is a polynomial that is the sum or the difference of two terms, each of which is a monomial. ✓ To multiply two binomials, use "FOIL" method. (First–Out–In–Last) $(x + a)(x + b) = x \times x + x \times b + a \times x + a \times b = x^2 + bx + ax + ab$
Example	*Multiply.* $(x - 4)(x + 9) =$ **Solution:** Use "FOIL". (First–Out–In–Last): $(x - 4)(x + 9) = x^2 + 9x - 4x - 36$ Then simplify: $x^2 + 9x - 4x - 36 = x^2 + 5x - 36$
Your Turn!	1) $(x + 2)(x + 2) =$ _____ 2) $(x + 3)(x + 2) =$ _____ 3) $(x - 3)(x + 4) =$ _____ 4) $(x - 2)(x - 4) =$ _____ 5) $(x + 3)(x + 4) =$ _____ 6) $(x + 5)(x + 4) =$ _____ 7) $(x - 6)(x - 5) =$ _____ 8) $(x - 5)(x - 5) =$ _____ 9) $(x + 6)(x - 8) =$ _____ 10) $(x - 9)(x + 7) =$ _____

Name: ....   **Date:** ....

Topic	*Factoring Trinomials*
Notes	To factor trinomial, use of the following methods: ✓ "FOIL": $(x + a)(x + b) = x^2 + (b + a)x + ab$ ✓ "Difference of Squares": $$a^2 - b^2 = (a + b)(a - b)$$ $$a^2 + 2ab + b^2 = (a + b)(a + b)$$ $$a^2 - 2ab + b^2 = (a - b)(a - b)$$ ✓ "Reverse FOIL": $x^2 + (b + a)x + ab = (x + a)(x + b)$
Example	*Factor this trinomial.* $x^2 + 12x + 32 =$ **Solution:** Break the expression into groups: $(x^2 + 4x) + (8x + 32)$ Now factor out x from $x^2 + 4x : x(x + 4)$, and factor out 8 from $8x + 32$: $8(x + 4)$ Then: $(x^2 + 4x) + (8x + 32) = x(x + 4) + 8(x + 4)$ Now factor out like term: $(x + 4) \rightarrow (x + 4)(x + 8)$

Your Turn!	1) $x^2 + 6x + 9 =$ ———	2) $x^2 + 5x + 6 =$ ———
	3) $x^2 + x + 12 =$ ———	4) $x^2 - 6x + 8 =$ ———
	5) $x^2 + 7x + 12 =$ ———	6) $x^2 + 12x + 32 =$ ———
	7) $x^2 - 11x + 30 =$ ———	8) $x^2 - 14x + 45 =$ ———

Answers– Chapter 10

Simplifying Polynomials

1) $-2x + 4$
2) $4x + 12$
3) $9x^2 - 12x$
4) $10x^2 + 40x$
5) $-10x^2 - 7x$

6) $-33x^2 + 12x$
7) $x^2 + 9x + 20$
8) $x^2 + 10x + 16$
9) $10x^3 + x^2$
10) $2x^5 + 10x^4$

Adding and Subtracting Polynomials

1) $5x^2 - x - 5$
2) $x^3 + x - 2$
3) $7x^2 - 5x - 5$
4) $5x^2 - 9$
5) $7x^2$

6) $x^2 + 10$
7) $4x^3 - 3x$
8) $7x^4 - 2x$
9) $11x^3 + 1$
10) $-x^3 + 2x^2 - 7$

Multiplying Monomials

1) $8x^8$
2) $30x^{11}$
3) $-12x^5 y^6$
4) $-15x^8 y^5$

5) $40x^{13} y^8$
6) $18x^{16} y^{13}$
7) $36x^{12} y^{11} z^5$
8) $-56x^{15} y^{14} z^{16}$

Multiplying and Dividing Monomials

1) $x^9 y^3$
2) $x^6 y^6$
3) $2x^{12} y^6$
4) $12x^{11} y^7$

5) $-24x^{14} y^{16}$
6) $-18x^{16} y^{11}$
7) $5x^3 y^5$
8) $-6x^4 y^7$

Multiplying a Polynomial and a Monomial

1) $6x^2 + 3xy$
2) $x^2 - 3xy$
3) $-5x^2 + 3xy$
4) $4x^2 + 20xy$

5) $-5x^2 - 8xy$
6) $12x^2 - 14xy$
7) $-3x^4 - 12xy^2 + 18x^2$
8) $7x^3 - 35xy^2 + 28x$

Multiplying Binomials

1) $x^2 + 4x + 4$
2) $x^2 + 5x + 6$
3) $x^2 + x - 12$
4) $x^2 - 6x + 8$
5) $x^2 + 7x + 12$

6) $x^2 + 9x + 20$
7) $x^2 - 11x + 30$
8) $x^2 - 10x + 25$
9) $x^2 - 2x - 48$
10) $x^2 - 2x - 63$

Factoring Trinomials

1) $(x + 3)(x + 3)$
2) $(x + 3)(x + 2)$
3) $(x - 3)(x + 4)$
4) $(x - 2)(x - 4)$

5) $(x + 3)(x + 4)$
6) $(x + 8)(x + 4)$
7) $(x - 6)(x - 5)$
8) $(x - 9)(x - 5)$

Chapter 11:

Geometry and Solid Figures

Topics that you'll practice in this chapter:

✓ The Pythagorean Theorem

✓ Complementary and Supplementary angle

✓ Parallel lines and Transversals

✓ Triangles

✓ Special Right Triangles

✓ Polygons

✓ Trapezoids

✓ Cubes

✓ Rectangular Prism

✓ Cylinder

Name: ....

Date: ....

Topic	*The Pythagorean Theorem*
Notes	✓ In any right triangle: $a^2 + b^2 = c^2$
Example	Right triangle ABC (not shown) has two legs of lengths 18 cm (AB) and 24 cm (AC). What is the length of the third side (BC)? **Solution:** Use Pythagorean Theorem: $a^2 + b^2 = c^2$ Then: $a^2 + b^2 = c^2 \rightarrow 18^2 + 24^2 = c^2 \rightarrow 324 + 576 = c^2$ $c^2 = 900 \rightarrow c = \sqrt{900} = 30\ cm$
Your Turn!	1) _____ 2) _____ 15, 8, ? 34, 16, ? 3) _____ 4) _____ 13, 5, ? 15, 12, ?

Name:	Date: ....

Topic	**Complementary and Supplementary Angles**
Notes	✓ Complementary angles are two angles with a sum of $90°$. A common case is when they form a right angle. ✓ Supplementary angles are two angles with a sum of $180°$. A common case is when they lie on the same side of a straight line. $60°$ $30°$ $130°$ $50°$
Example	**Find the missing angle.** $x = ?$ $43°$ **Solution:** Notice that two angles form a straight angle when together. This means that the angles are supplementary and have a sum of $180°$. $x + 43 = 180 \rightarrow x = 180 - 43 = 137°$
Your Turn!	*Find the missing measurement in the pair of angles.* 1) $x =$ ___ $114°$ $x = ?$ 2) $x =$ ___ $55°$ $x = ?$

Name:	Date: ....

Topic	***Parallel lines and Transversals***

Notes	☑ When a line (transversal) intersects two parallel lines in the same plane, eight angles are formed. In the following diagram, a transversal intersects two parallel lines. Angles 1, 7, 3, and 5 are congruent. Angles 2, 8, 4, and 6 are also congruent.
	☑ In the following diagram, the following angles are supplementary angles (their sum is 180):
	   - Angles 1 and 8
	   - Angles 2 and 7
	   - Angles 3 and 6
	   - Angles 4 and 5

Example	***In the following diagram, two parallel lines are cut by a transversal. What is the value of*** x***?*** **Solution:** The two angles 75° and $11x - 2$ are equal. $11x - 2 = 75$ Now, solve for x: $11x - 2 + 2 = 75 + 2 \rightarrow$ $11x = 77 \rightarrow x = \dfrac{77}{11} \rightarrow x = 7$
Your Turn!	2) Find the measure of the angle indicated. ? = ___ 3) Solve for x. $x =$ ___

Name: .... **Date:** ....

Topic	*Triangles*
Notes	✓ In any triangle the sum of all angles is 180 degrees. ✓ Area of a triangle = $\frac{1}{2}(base \times height)$
Example	What is the area of the following triangle? **Solution:** Use the area formula: Area $= \frac{1}{2}(base \times height)$ $base = 16$ and $height = 6$ Area $= \frac{1}{2}(16 \times 6) = \frac{96}{2} = 48$
Your Turn!	1) _____ 24, 10 2) _____ 18, 28 3) _____ 20, 30 4) _____ 32, 46

| Name: .... | Date: .... |

Topic	*Special Right Triangles*
Notes	✓ A special right triangle is a triangle whose sides are in a particular ratio. Two special right triangles are $45° - 45° - 90°$ and $30° - 60° - 90°$ triangles. ✓ In a special $45° - 45° - 90°$ triangle, the three angles are $45°$, $45°$ and $90°$. The lengths of the sides of this triangle are in the ratio of $1:1:\sqrt{2}$. ✓ In a special triangle $30° - 60° - 90°$, the three angles are $30° - 60° - 90°$. The lengths of this triangle are in the ratio of $1:\sqrt{3}:2$. (30° at top, $a\sqrt{3}$ on left side, $2a$ on hypotenuse, 60° at bottom, a at base)
Example	*Find the length of the hypotenuse of a right triangle if the length of the other two sides are both 5 inches.* ***Solution:*** this is a right triangle with two equal sides. Therefore, it must be a $45° - 45° - 90°$ triangle. ***Two equal sides are*** 5 *inches. So, t*he length of the hypotenuse is $5\sqrt{2}$ *inches. If the first and second value of the ratio* $x: x: x\sqrt{2}$. $$x: x: x\sqrt{2} \rightarrow x = 5 \rightarrow 5: 5: 5\sqrt{2}$$
Your Turn!	**Find the value of x and y in each triangle.** 1) $x = $ ___ $y = $ ___ (triangle with x on hypotenuse top, 12 on right side, 30° at bottom left, y at base) 2) $x = $ ___ $y = $ ___ (triangle with 7 on left, y on hypotenuse, right angle at bottom left, 45° at bottom right, x at base)

Name: ....

Date: ....

Topic	*Polygons*
Notes	Perimeter of a square $= 4 \times side = 4s$ Perimeter of a rectangle $= 2(width + length)$ Perimeter of trapezoid $= a + b + c + d$ Perimeter of a regular hexagon $= 6a$ Perimeter of a parallelogram $= 2(l + w)$
Example	*Find the perimeter of following regular hexagon.* **Solution:** Since the hexagon is regular, all sides are equal. Then: Perimeter of Hexagon $= 6 \times (one\ side)$ Perimeter of Hexagon $= 6 \times (one\ side) = 6 \times 9 = 54\ m$
Your Turn!	1) *(rectangle)* _____ $9\ in$ $15\ in$ 2) _____ $8\ m$ $10\ m$ $10\ m$ $14\ m$ 3) *(regular hexagon)* _____ $5\ m$ 4) *(parallelogram)* _____ $10\ in$ $16\ in$

Name: .... 　　 Date: ....

Topic	*Cubes*
Notes	✓ A cube is a three-dimensional solid object bounded by six square sides. ✓ Volume is the measure of the amount of space inside of a solid figure, like a cube, ball, cylinder or pyramid. ✓ Volume of a cube $= (one\ side)^3$ ✓ surface area of cube $= 6 \times (one\ side)^2$
Example	Find the volume and surface area of the following cube. 　 15 *cm* **Solution:** Use volume formula: $volume = (one\ side)^3$ Then: $volume = (one\ side)^3 = (15)^3 = 3,375\ cm^3$ Use surface area formula: $surface\ area\ of\ cube: 6(one\ side)^2 = 6(15)^2 = 6(225) = 1,350\ cm^2$
Your Turn!	***Find the volume of each cube.*** 1) _____ 　　　　　　　　 2) _____ 　　 11 *in* 　　　　　　　　　 13 *ft* 3) _____ 　　　　　　　　 4) _____ 　 14 *cm* 　　　　　　　　　 30 *m*

Name:	Date: ....

Topic	*Trapezoids*
Notes	✓ A quadrilateral with at least one pair of parallel sides is a trapezoid. ✓ Area of a trapezoid $= \frac{1}{2}h(b_1 + b_2)$ b_2 h b_1
Example	Calculate the area of the trapezoid. **Solution:** Use area formula: $A = \frac{1}{2}h(b_1 + b_2)$ $b_1 = 8\ cm$, $b_2 = 12\ cm$ and $h = 14\ cm$ Then: $A = \frac{1}{2}(14)(12 + 8) = 7(20) = 140\ cm^2$ $12\ cm$ $14\ cm$ $8\ cm$
Your Turn!	1) _____ $5\ cm$ $4\ cm$ $9\ cm$ 2) _____ $8\ m$ $10\ m$ $12\ m$ 3) _____ $7\ ft$ $6\ ft$ $15\ ft$ 4) _____ $10\ cm$ $8\ cm$ $14\ cm$

Name:	Date: ....

Topic	**_Rectangular Prisms_**
Notes	✓ A solid 3-dimensional object which has six rectangular faces. ✓ Volume of a Rectangular prism = **_Length × Width × Height_** $Volume = l \times w \times h$ $Surface\ area = 2(wh + lw + lh)$
Example	Find the volume and surface area of rectangular prism. **Solution:** Use volume formula: $Volume = l \times w \times h$ Then: $Volume = 4 \times 2 \times 6 = 48\ m^3$ Use surface area formula: $Surface\ area = 2(wh + lw + lh)$ Then: $Surface\ area = 2\big((2 \times 6) + (4 \times 2) + (4 \times 6)\big)$ $= 2(12 + 8 + 24) = 2(44) = 88\ m^2$
Your Turn!	**_Find the surface area of each Rectangular Prism._** 1) _____ 6 ft 10 ft 4 ft 2) _____ 8 cm 16 cm 6 cm 3) _____ 12 m 18 m 10 m 4) _____ 20 in 15 in 12 in

Name: ....

Date: ....

Topic	*Cylinder*
Notes	✓ A cylinder is a solid geometric figure with straight parallel sides and a circular or oval cross section. ✓ *Volume of Cylinder Formula* $= \pi(radius)^2 \times height$ $\pi = 3.14$ ✓ *Surface area of a cylinder* $= 2\pi r^2 + 2\pi rh$ *height* *radius*
Example	*Find the volume and Surface area of the follow Cylinder.* **Solution:** Use volume formula: $Volume = \pi(radius)^2 \times height$ Then: $Volume = \pi(3)^2 \times 12 = 9\pi \times 12 = 108\pi$ $\pi = 3.14$ **then:** $Volume = 108\pi = 339.12 \; cm^3$ Use surface area formula: $Surface \; area = 2\pi r^2 + 2\pi rh$ **Then:** $2\pi(3)^2 + 2\pi(3)(12) = 2\pi(9) + 2\pi(36) = 18\pi + 72\pi = 90\pi$ $\pi = 3.14$ **Then:** $Surface \; area = 90 \times 3.14 = 282.6 \; cm^2$ *12 cm* *3 cm*
Your Turn!	*Find the volume of each Cylinder.* ($\pi = 3.14$) 1) _____ *10 in.* *2 in.* 2) _____ *14 m* *5 m* *Find the Surface area of each Cylinder.* ($\pi = 3.14$) 3) _____ *15 ft.* *9 ft.* 4) _____ *20 cm* *12 cm*

Answers– Chapter 11

The Pythagorean Theorem

1) 17
2) 30
3) 12
4) 9

Complementary and Supplementary Angles

1) $66°$
2) $35°$

Parallel lines and Transversals

3) $80°$
4) -7

Triangles

1) 120
2) 252
3) 300
4) 736

Special Right Triangles

1) $x = 24 \ \ y = 12\sqrt{3}$
2) $x = 7 \ \ y = 7\sqrt{2}$

Polygons

1) $48 \ in$
2) $42 \ m$
3) $30 \ m$
4) $52 \ in$

Cubes

1) $1,331 \ in^3$
2) $2,197 \ ft^3$
3) $2,744 \ cm^3$
4) $27,000 \ m^3$

Trapezoids

1) $28 \ cm^2$
2) $100 \ m^2$
3) $66 \ ft^2$
4) $96 \ cm^2$

Circle

1) $113.04 \ cm^2$
2) $314 \ in^2$
3) $50.24 \ cm$
4) $37.68 \ m$

Rectangular Prism

1) $248 \ ft^2$
2) $544 \ cm^2$
3) $1,032 \ m^2$
4) $1,440 \ in^2$

Cylinder

1) $125.6 \ in^3$
2) $1,099 \ m^3$
3) $1,356.48 \ ft^2$
4) $2,411.52 \ cm^2$

Chapter 12:

Statistics

Topics that you'll practice in this chapter:

- ✓ Mean, Median , Mode , and Range of the Given Data
- ✓ Pie Graph
- ✓ Probability Problems
- ✓ Permutations and Combinations

Name: .... **Date:** ....

Topic	*Mean, Median, Mode, and Range of the Given Data*
Notes	✓ Mean: $\dfrac{sum\ of\ the\ data}{total\ number\ of\ data\ entires}$ ✓ Mode: value in the list that appears most often. ✓ Median: is the middle number of a group of numbers that have been arranged in order by size. ✓ Range: the difference of largest value and smallest value in the list.
Example	*Find the mode and median of these numbers?* $16, 10, 6, 3, 1, 16, 2, 4$ **Solution:** Mode: value in the list that appears most often. Number 16 is the value in the list that appears most often (there are two number 16). To find median, write the numbers in order: $1, 2, 3, 4, 6, 10, 16, 16$ Number 4 and 6 are in the middle. Find their average: $\dfrac{4+6}{2} = \dfrac{10}{2} = 5$ The median is 5.

Your Turn!	1) $3, 2, 4, 8, 3, 10$ Mode: _____ Range: _____ Mean: _____ Median: _____	2) $6, 3, 2, 9, 5, 7, 2, 14$ Mode: _____ Range: _____ Mean: _____ Median: _____
	3) $5, 4, 3, 2, 9, 5, 6, 8, 12$ Mode: _____ Range: _____ Mean: _____ Median: _____	4) $12, 6, 8, 6, 9, 6, 4, 13$ Mode: _____ Range: _____ Mean: _____ Median: _____

Name:	Date: ....

Topic	*Pie Graph*
Notes	✓ A Pie Chart is a circle chart divided into sectors, each sector represents the relative size of each value.
Example	A library has 460 books that include Mathematics, Physics, Chemistry, English and History. Use following graph to answer the question. **What is the number of Physics books?** **Solution:** Number of total books $= 460$ Percent of Physics books $= 25\% = 0.25$ Then, umber of Physics books: $$0.25 \times 460 = 115$$
Your Turn!	The circle graph below shows all Mr. Smith's expenses for last month. Mr. Smith spent \$440 for clothes last month. Mr. Smith's last month expenses
	1) How much did Mr. Smith spend for his Books last month? _____ 2) How much did Mr. Smith spend for Bills last month? _____ 3) How much did Mr. Smith spend for his foods last month? _____

Name: ....   Date: ....

Topic	*Probability Problems*
Notes	✓ Probability is the likelihood of something happening in the future. It is expressed as a number between zero (can never happen) to 1 (will always happen). ✓ Probability can be expressed as a fraction, a decimal, or a percent. ✓ Probability formula: $Probability = \frac{number\ of\ desired\ outcomes}{number\ of\ total\ outcomes}$
Example	If there are 3 green balls, 4 red balls, and 10 blue balls in a basket, what is the probability that Jason will pick out a red ball from the basket? **Solution:** There are 4 red ball and 17 are total number of balls. Therefore, probability that Jason will pick out a red ball from the basket is 4 out of 17 or $\frac{4}{3+4+10} = \frac{4}{17}$
Your Turn!	1) A number is chosen at random from 1 to 20. Find the probability of selecting a prime number. (A prime number is a whole number that is only divisible by itself and 1) _____ 2) There are only red and blue cards in a box. The probability of choosing a red card in the box at random is one third. If there are 24 blue cards, how many cards are in the box? _____ 3) A die is rolled, what is the probability that an even number is obtained? _____

Name:	Date: ....

Topic	*Permutations and Combinations*
Notes	✓ Permutations: The number of ways to choose a sample of k elements from a set of n distinct objects where order does matter, and replacements are not allowed. For a permutation problem, use this formula: $$_nP_k = \frac{n!}{(n-k)!}$$ ✓ Combination: The number of ways to choose a sample of r elements from a set of n distinct objects where order does not matter, and replacements are not allowed. For a combination problem, use this formula: $$_nC_r = \frac{n!}{r!\,(n-r)!}$$ ✓ Factorials are products, indicated by an exclamation mark. For example, 4! Equals: $4 \times 3 \times 2 \times 1$. Remember that 0! is defined to be equal to 1.
Example	*How many ways can we pick a team of* 4 *people from a group of* 8? **Solution:** Since the order doesn't matter, we need to use combination formula where n is 8 and r is 4. Then: $\frac{n!}{r!\,(n-r)!} = \frac{8!}{4!\,(8-4)!} = \frac{8!}{4!\,(4)!} = \frac{8\times7\times6\times5\times4!}{4!\,(4)!} = \frac{8\times7\times6\times5}{4\times3\times2\times1} = \frac{1,680}{24} = 70$
Your Turn!	1) In how many ways can 8 athletes be arranged in a straight line? _____ 2) How many ways can we award a first and second place prize among eight contestants? _____ 3) In how many ways can we choose 3 players from a team of 9 players? _____

Answers– Chapter 12

Mean, Median, Mode, and Range of the Given Data

1) Mode: 3   Mean: 5   Range: 8   Median: 3.5
2) Mode: 2   Mean: 6   Range: 12   Median: 5.5
3) Mode: 5   Mean: 6   Range: 10   Median: 5
4) Mode: 6   Mean: 8   Range: 9   Median: 7

Pie *Graph*

1) $308
2) $396
3) $550

Probability Problems

1) $\frac{8}{20} = \frac{2}{5}$

2) 36

3) $\frac{1}{2}$

Combinations and Permutations

1) 40,320
2) 56
3) 84

Chapter 13:

Functions Operations

Topics that you'll practice in this chapter:

- ✓ Function Notation and Evaluation
- ✓ Adding and Subtracting Functions
- ✓ Multiplying and Dividing Functions
- ✓ Position of Functions
- ✓ Functions Inverses

Name: ....   Date: ....

Topic	Function Notation and Evaluation
Notes	✓ Functions are mathematical operations that assign unique outputs to given inputs. ✓ Function notation is the way a function is written. It is meant to be a precise way of giving information about the function without a rather lengthy written explanation. ✓ The most popular function notation is $f(x)$ which is read "f of x". ✓ To evaluate a function, plug in the input (the given value or expression) for the function's variable (place holder, x).
Example	*Evaluate*: $h(n) = 2n^2 - 2$, find $h(2)$. **Solution:** Substitute n with 2: Then: $h(n) = 2n^2 - 2 \rightarrow h(2) = 2(2)^2 - 2 = 8 - 2 \rightarrow h(2) = 6$

Your Turn!	1) $f(x) = x - 2$, find $f(-1)$	2) $g(x) = 2x + 4$, find $g(3)$
	3) $g(n) = 2n - 8$, find $g(-1)$	4) $h(n) = n^2 - 1$, find $h(-2)$
	5) $f(x) = x^2 + 12$, find $f(5)$	6) $g(x) = 2x^2 - 9$, find $g(-2)$
	7) $w(x) = 2x^2 - 4x$, find $w(2n)$	8) $p(x) = 4x^3 - 10$, find $p(-3a)$

Name:	Date: ....

Topic	**Adding and Subtracting Functions**
Notes	✓ Just like we can add and subtract numbers and expressions, we can add or subtract two functions and simplify or evaluate them. The result is a new function. ✓ For two functions $f(x)$ and $g(x)$, we can create two new functions: $(f + g)(x) = f(x) + g(x)$ and $(f - g)(x) = f(x) - g(x)$
Example	$g(a) = 2a - 5$, $f(a) = a + 8$, **Find:** $(g + f)(a)$ **Solution:** $(g + f)(a) = g(a) + f(a)$ Then: $(g + f)(a) = (2a - 5) + (a + 8) = 3a + 3$

Your Turn!	1) $g(x) = x - 2$ $h(x) = 2x + 6$ Find: $(h + g)(3)$ _____	2) $f(x) = 3x + 2$ $g(x) = -x - 6$ Find: $(f + g)(2)$ _____
	3) $f(x) = 5x + 8$ $g(x) = 3x - 12$ Find: $(f - g)(-2)$ _____	4) $h(x) = 2x^2 - 10$ $g(x) = 3x + 12$ Find: $(h + g)(3)$ _____
	5) $g(x) = 12x - 8$ $h(x) = 3x^2 + 14$ Find: $(h - g)(x)$ _____	6) $h(x) = -2x^2 - 18$ $g(x) = 4x^2 + 15$ Find: $(h - g)(a)$ _____

Name: ....

Date: ....

Topic	*Multiplying and Dividing Functions*
Notes	✓ Just like we can multiply and divide numbers and expressions, we can multiply and divide two functions and simplify or evaluate them. ✓ For two functions $f(x)$ and $g(x)$, we can create two new functions: $(f.g)(x) = f(x).g(x)$ and $\left(\frac{f}{g}\right)(x) = \frac{f(x)}{g(x)}$
Example	$g(x) = x + 5$, $f(x) = x - 3$, Find: $(g.f)(2)$ **Solution:** $(g.f)(x) = g(x).f(x) = (x + 5)(x - 3) = x^2 - 3x + 5x - 15 = x^2 + 2x - 15$ Substitute x with 2: $(g.f)(x) = (2)^2 + 2(2) - 15 = 4 + 4 - 15 = -7$

Your Turn!	1) $g(x) = x - 5$ $h(x) = x + 6$ Find: $(g.h)(-1)$ _____	2) $f(x) = 2x + 2$ $g(x) = -x - 6$ Find: $(\frac{f}{g})(-2)$ _____
	3) $f(x) = 5x + 3$ $g(x) = 2x - 4$ Find: $(\frac{f}{g})(5)$ _____	4) $h(x) = x^2 - 2$ $g(x) = x + 4$ Find: $(g.h)(3)$ _____
	5) $g(x) = 4x - 12$ $h(x) = x^2 + 4$ Find: $(g.h)(-2)$ _____	6) $h(x) = 3x^2 - 8$ $g(x) = 4x + 6$ Find: $(\frac{f}{g})(-4)$ _____

Name:	Date: ....

Topic	*Composition of Functions*	
Notes	✓ "Composition of functions" simply means combining two or more functions in a way where the output from one function becomes the input for the next function. ✓ The notation used for composition is: $(f \circ g)(x) = f(g(x))$ and is read "f composed with g of x" or "f of g of x".	
Example	*Using $f(x) = x - 8$ and $g(x) = x + 2$, find:* $(f \circ g)(3)$ **Solution:** $(f \circ g)(x) = f(g(x))$ *Then:* $(f \circ g)(x) = f(g(x)) = f(x + 2) = x + 2 - 8 = x - 6$ Substitute x with 3: $(f \circ g)(3) = f(g(3)) = 3 - 6 = -3$	
Your Turn!	1) $f(x) = 2x$ $g(x) = x + 3$ Find: $(fog)(2)$ _____	2) $f(x) = x + 2$ $g(x) = x - 6$ Find: $(fog)(-1)$ _____
	3) $f(x) = 3x$ $g(x) = x + 4$ Find: $(gof)(4)$ _____	4) $h(x) = 2x - 2$ $g(x) = x + 4$ Find: $(goh)(2)$ _____
	5) $f(x) = 2x - 8$ $g(x) = x + 10$ Find: $(fog)(-2)$ _____	6) $f(x) = x^2 - 8$ $g(x) = 2x + 3$ Find: $(gof)(4)$ _____

Name:	Date: ....

Topic	*Function Inverses*
Notes	✓ An inverse function is a function that reverses another function: if the function f applied to an input x gives a result of y, then applying its inverse function g to y gives the result x. $f(x) = y$ if and only if $g(y) = x$
Example	**1) Find the inverse of** $f(x) = 4x + 2$ **Solution: First, replace** $f(x)$ **with** y: $y = 4x + 2$ **Next, replace all** $x's$ **with** y **and all** $y's$ **with** x: $x = 4y + 2$ **Now, solve for** y: $x = 4y + 2 \rightarrow x - 2 = 4y \rightarrow \frac{1}{4}x - \frac{1}{2} = y$ **Finally replace** y **with** $f^{-1}(x)$: $f^{-1}(x) = \frac{1}{4}x - \frac{1}{2}$ **2) Find the inverse of** $h(x) = \frac{x+1}{2}$ **Solution:** $h(x) = \frac{x+1}{2} \rightarrow y = \frac{x+1}{2}$, **replace all** $x's$ **with** y **and all** $y's$ **with** x: $x = \frac{y+1}{2} \rightarrow 2x = y + 1 \rightarrow 2x - 1 = y \rightarrow h^{-1}(x) = 2x - 1$

Your Turn!	**Find the inverse of each function.**
	
	1) $f(x) = -\frac{1}{x} - 9$ **2)** $g(x) = \sqrt{x} - 2$
	  $f^{-1}(x) = $ _____ $g^{-1}(x) = $ _____
	
	3) $h(x) = -\frac{5}{x+3}$ **4)** $f(x) = 6x + 6$
	  $h^{-1}(x) = $ _____ $f^{-1}(x) = $ _____

Answers - Chapter 13

Function Notation and Evaluation

1) $f(-1) = -3$
2) $g(3) = 10$
3) $g(-1) = -10$
4) $h(-2) = 3$
5) $f(5) = 37$
6) $g(-2) = -1$
7) $w(2n) = 8n^2 - 8n$
8) $p(-3a) = -108a^3 + 30a$

Adding and Subtracting Functions

1) 13
2) 0
3) 16
4) 29
5) $3x^2 - 12x + 22$
6) $-6a^2 - 33$

Multiplying and Dividing Functions

1) -30
2) $\frac{1}{2}$
3) $\frac{14}{3}$
4) 49
5) -160
6) -4

Composition of Functions

1) 10
2) -5
3) 16
4) 6
5) 8
6) 19

Function Inverses

1) $f^{-1}(x) = -\frac{1}{x+9}$
2) $g^{-1}(x) = x^2 + 4x + 4$
3) $h^{-1}(x) = -\frac{5}{x} - 3$
4) $f^{-1}(x) = \frac{x-6}{6}$

Chapter 14:

Quadratic

Topics that you'll practice in this chapter:

✓ Solving a Quadratic Equation

✓ Graphing Quadratic Functions

✓ Solving Quadratic Inequalities

✓ Graphing Quadratic Inequalities

Name:	Date: ....

Topic	**Solving a Quadratic Equation**
Notes	✓ Write the equation in the form of: $ax^2 + bx + c = 0$ ✓ Factor the quadratic and solve for the variable. ✓ Use quadratic formula if you couldn't factorize the quadratic. ✓ Quadratic formula: $x = \frac{-b \pm \sqrt{b^2 - 4ac}}{2a}$
Example	**Find the solutions of quadratic.** $x^2 + x - 72 = 0$ **Solution:** Use quadratic formula: $x = \frac{-b \pm \sqrt{b^2 - 4ac}}{2a}$, $a = 1, b = 1$ and $c = -72$ $x = \frac{-1 \pm \sqrt{1^2 - 4 \times 1(-72)}}{2 \times 1}$ $x_1 = \frac{-1 + \sqrt{1^2 - 4 \times 1 \times (-7\ )}}{2 \times 1} = 8$, $x_2 = \frac{-1 - \sqrt{1^2 - 4 \times 1 \times (-7\ )}}{2 \times 1} = -9$

Your Turn!		
	1) $x^2 - x - 2 = 0$ $x = \underline{\quad}, x = \underline{\quad}$	2) $x^2 - 6x + 8 = 0$ $x = \underline{\quad}, x = \underline{\quad}$
	3) $x^2 - 4x + 3 = 0$ $x = \underline{\quad}, x = \underline{\quad}$	4) $x^2 + x - 12 = 0$ $x = \underline{\quad}, x = \underline{\quad}$
	5) $x^2 + 7x - 18 = 0$ $x = \underline{\quad}, x = \underline{\quad}$	6) $x^2 - 2x - 15 = 0$ $x = \underline{\quad}, x = \underline{\quad}$
	7) $x^2 + 6x - 40 = 0$ $x = \underline{\quad}, x = \underline{\quad}$	8) $x^2 - 9x - 36 = 0$ $x = \underline{\quad}, x = \underline{\quad}$

Name: .... **Date:** ....

Topic	*Graphing Quadratic Functions*
Notes	✓ Quadratic functions in vertex form: $y = a(x - h)^2 + k$ where (h, k) is the vertex of the function. The axis of symmetry is $x = h$ ✓ Quadratic functions in standard form: $y = ax^2 + bx + c$ where $x = -\frac{b}{2a}$ is the value of x in the vertex of the function. ✓ To graph a quadratic function, first find the vertex, then substitute some values for x and solve for y.
Example	*Sketch the graph of* $y = (x - 2)^2 - 5$ **Solution:** *The vertex of* $y = (x - 2)^2 - 5$ *is* $(2, 5)$. Substitute zero for x and solve for y. $\qquad y = (0 - 2)^2 - 5 = -1$ The y-_Intercept_ is $(0, -1)$ Now, you can simply graph the quadratic function.
Your Turn!	1) $y = (x - 4)^2 - 2$ 2) $y = 2(x + 2)^2 - 3$

| Name: .... | Date: .... |

Topic	*Solving Quadratic Inequalities*
Notes	✓ A quadratic inequality is one that can be written in the standard form of $ax^2 + bx + c > 0$ (or substitute $<, \leq,$ or $\geq$ for $>$). ✓ Solving a quadratic inequality is like solving equations. We need to find the solutions (the zeroes). ✓ To solve quadratic inequalities, first find quadratic equations. Then choose a test value between zeroes. Finally, find interval(s), such as > 0 or < 0.
Example	**Solve quadratic inequality.** $x^2 + x - 12 > 0$ **Solution:** First solve $x^2 + x - 12 = 0$ by factoring. Then: $x^2 + x - 6 = 0 \rightarrow$ $(x - 3)(x + 4) = 0$. The product of two expressions is 0. Then: $(x - 3) = 0 \rightarrow x = 3$ or $(x + 4) = 0 \rightarrow x = -4$. Now, choose a value between 3 and -4. Let's choose 0. Then: $x = 0 \rightarrow x^2 + x - 12 > 0 \rightarrow (0)^2 + (0) - 12 > 0 \rightarrow -12 > 0$ -12 is not greater than 0. Therefore, all values between 3 and -4 are NOT the solution of this quadratic inequality. The solution is: $x > 3$ and $x < -4$.
Your Turn!	1) $x^2 - 6x - 27 > 0$ _____ 2) $x^2 + 13x + 42 < 0$ _____ 3) $x^2 + x - 56 > 0$ _____ 4) $x^2 - 15x + 54 < 0$ _____ 5) $x^2 + 2x - 35 \leq 0$ _____ 6) $x^2 - x - 72 \geq 0$ _____

Name: ....

Date: ....

Topic	*Graphing Quadratic Inequalities*
Notes	✓ A quadratic inequality is in the form $y > ax^2 + bx + c$ (or substitute $<, \leq,$ or $\geq$ for $>$). ✓ To graph a quadratic inequality, start by graphing the quadratic parabola. Then fill in the region either inside or outside of it, depending on the inequality. ✓ Choose a testing point and check the solution section.
Example	**Sketch the graph of $y > x^2$** **Solution:** First, graph $y = x^2$ Since, the inequality sing is $>$, we need to use dash lines. Now, choose a testing point inside the parabola. Let's choose $(0,2)$. $y > x^2 \rightarrow 2 > (0)^2 \rightarrow 2 > 0$ This is true. So, inside the parabola is the solution section.
Your Turn!	1) $y \leq x^2 + 4x + 5$ 2) $y \leq x^2 + 2x - 3$

Answers - Chapter 14

Solving a Quadratic Equation

1) $x = 2, x = -1$
2) $x = 2, x = 4$
3) $x = 3, x = 1$
4) $x = 3, x = -4$

5) $x = 2, x = -9$
6) $x = 5, x = -3$
7) $x = 4, x = -10$
8) $x = 12, x = -3$

Graphing Quadratic Functions

1) $y = (x - 4)^2 - 2$

2) $y = 2(x + 2)^2 - 3$

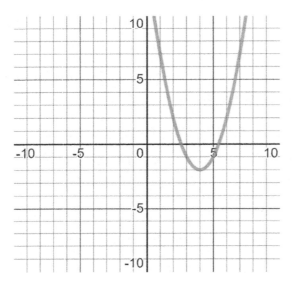

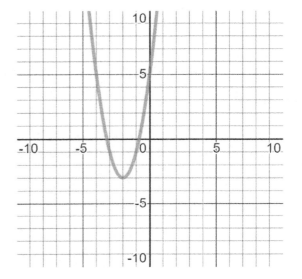

Solving Quadratic Inequalities

1) $x < -3 \ or \ x > 9$
2) $-7 < x < -6$
3) $x < -8 \ or \ x > 7$

4) $6 < x < 9$
5) $-7 \leq x \leq 5$
6) $x \leq -8 \ or \ x \geq 9$

Graphing Quadratic Inequalities

1) $y \leq x^2 + 4x + 5$

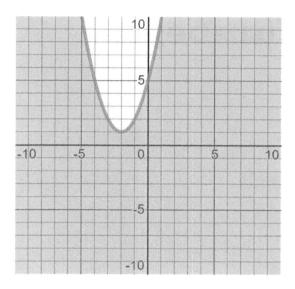

2) $y \leq x^2 + 2x - 3$

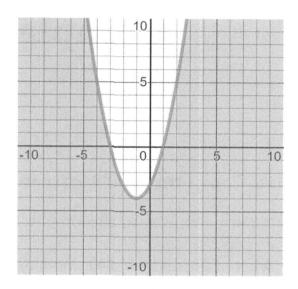

Chapter 15:

Complex Numbers

Math Topics that you'll learn in this Chapter:

✓ Adding and Subtracting Complex Numbers

✓ Multiplying and Dividing Complex Numbers

✓ Rationalizing Imaginary Denominators

Name:	Date: ....

Topic	*Adding and Subtracting Complex Numbers*
Notes	✓ A complex number is expressed in the form $a + bi$, where a and b are real numbers, and i, which is called an imaginary number, is a solution of the equation $x^2 = -1$ ✓ For adding complex numbers: $(a + bi) + (c + di) = (a + c) + (b + d)i$ ✓ For subtracting complex numbers: ✓ $(a + bi) - (c + di) = (a - c) + (b - d)i$
Example	Solve: $(14 + 7i) + (-5 - 3i)$ **Solution:** Remove parentheses: $(14 + 7i) + (-5 - 3i) \rightarrow 14 + 7i - 5 - 3i$ Combine like terms: $(14 - 5) + (7i - 3i) = 9 + 4i$
Your Turn!	1) $(5 - 3i) - (4 + i) =$ _____ 3) $(7 + 4i) - (5 - 6i) =$ _____ 5) $(-8 + 2i) - (5 - 3i) =$ _____ 7) $(-9 - 3i) - (9 - 10i) =$ _____ 2) $(2 + 6i) - (4 - 2i) =$ _____ 4) $(1 + 2i) + (5 - 7i) =$ _____ 6) $(7 - 9i) - (3 + 5i) =$ _____ 8) $(-12 - 4i) - (5 + 7i) =$ _____

Name: ....   **Date:** ....

Topic	*Multiplying and Dividing Complex Numbers*		
Notes	✓ Multiplying complex numbers: $(a+bi)+(c+di)=(ac-bd)+(ad+bc)i$ ✓ Dividing complex numbers: $\dfrac{a+bi}{c+d}=\dfrac{a+bi}{c+di}\times\dfrac{c-di}{c-di}=\dfrac{ac+bd}{c^2+d^2}+\dfrac{bc-ad}{c^2+d^2}i$ ✓ Imaginary number rule: $i^2=-1$		
Example	**Solve:** $\dfrac{8-2i}{2+i}$ **Solution:** Use the rule for dividing complex numbers: $$\dfrac{a+bi}{c+di}=\dfrac{a+bi}{c+di}\times\dfrac{c-di}{c-di}=\dfrac{ac+bd}{c^2+d^2}+\dfrac{bc-ad}{c^2+d^2}i\rightarrow$$ $$\dfrac{8-2i}{2+i}\times\dfrac{2-i}{2-i}=\dfrac{8\times(2)+(-2)(1)}{2^2+(1)^2}+\dfrac{-2\times(2)-(8)(1)}{2^2+(1)^2}i=\dfrac{14-12i}{5}$$ $$=\dfrac{14}{5}-\dfrac{12}{5}i$$		
Your Turn!	1) $(2-2i)(4-i)=$ _____		2) $(3-2i)(2-i)=$ _____
	3) $(3-i)(2-4i)=$ _____		4) $(6+i)(2-2i)=$ _____
	5) $\dfrac{5-i}{6+i}=$ _____		6) $\dfrac{7+2i}{3-2i}=$ _____

| Name: .... | Date: .... |

Topic	*Rationalizing Imaginary Denominators*
Notes	✓ Step 1: Find the conjugate (it's the denominator with different sign between the two terms. ✓ Step 2: Multiply numerator and denominator by the conjugate. ✓ Step 3: Simplify if needed.
Example	Solve: $\dfrac{6i}{3-3i}$ **Solution:** First, divide both sides of the fraction by 3: $\dfrac{6i}{3-3i} = \dfrac{2i}{1-i}$ Multiply both numerator and denominator by the conjugate $\dfrac{1+i}{1+i}$: $\dfrac{2i(1+i)}{(1-i)(1+i)} =$ Apply complex arithmetic rule: $(a+bi)(a-bi) = a^2 + b^2 \rightarrow (1-i)(1+i) =$ $1^2 + (1)^2 = 2$, then: $\dfrac{2i(1+i)}{(1-i)(1+i)} = \dfrac{2i+2i^2}{2} = \dfrac{2i+2i^2}{2} = \dfrac{2i}{2} + \dfrac{2(-1)}{2} = -1 + i$
Your Turn!	1) $\dfrac{2-i}{3i} =$ _____ 2) $\dfrac{4i+1}{2+i} =$ _____ 3) $\dfrac{6-3i}{3-i} =$ _____ 4) $\dfrac{8-3i}{2-i} =$ _____ 5) $\dfrac{-8+2i}{6-3i} =$ _____ 6) $\dfrac{-9+4i}{2-3i} =$ _____

Answers - Chapter 15

Adding and Subtracting Complex Numbers

1) $1 - 4i$
2) $-2 + 6i$
3) $2 + 10i$
4) $6 - 5i$

5) $-13 + 5i$
6) $4 - 14i$
7) $-18 + 7i$
8) $-17 - 11i$

Multiplying and Dividing Complex Numbers

1) $6 - 10i$
2) $4 - 7i$
3) $2 - 14i$
4) $14 - 10i$

5) $\frac{29}{37} - \frac{11}{37}i$

6) $\frac{17}{13} + \frac{20}{13}i$

Rationalizing Imaginary Denominators

1) $\frac{1}{3} + \frac{2}{3}i$
2) $\frac{6}{5} + \frac{7}{5}i$
3) $\frac{21}{10} - \frac{3}{10}i$

4) $\frac{19}{5} + \frac{2}{5}i$
5) $-\frac{6}{5} - \frac{4}{15}i$
6) $-\frac{30}{13} - \frac{19}{13}i$

Chapter 16:

Radicals

Topics that you'll practice in this chapter:

✓ Simplifying Radical Expressions

✓ Adding and Subtracting Radical Expressions

✓ Multiplying radical Expressions

✓ Simplifying Radical Expressions Involving Fractions

✓ Radical Equations

✓ Domain and Range of Radical Function

Name:	Date: ....

Topic	*Simplifying Radical Expressions*	
Notes	☑ Find the prime factors of the numbers or expressions inside the radical. ☑ Use radical properties to simplify the radical expression: $\sqrt[n]{x^a} = x^{\frac{a}{n}}$, $\sqrt[n]{xy} = x^{\frac{1}{n}} \times y^{\frac{1}{n}}$, $\sqrt[n]{\dfrac{x}{y}} = \dfrac{x^{\frac{1}{n}}}{y^{\frac{1}{n}}}$, and $\sqrt[n]{x} \times \sqrt[n]{y} = \sqrt[n]{xy}$	
Example	Evaluate. $\sqrt{64} \times \sqrt{y^2} =$ First factor the numbers: $64 = 8^2$ Then: $\sqrt{64} \times \sqrt{y^2} = \sqrt{8^2} \times \sqrt{y^2}$ Now use radical rule: $\sqrt[n]{a^n} = a$, Then: $\sqrt{8^2} \times \sqrt{y^2} = 8 \times y = 8y$	
Your Turn!	7) Evaluate. $\sqrt{49} =$ _____	8) Evaluate. $\sqrt{4} \times \sqrt{81} =$ _____
	9) Evaluate. $\sqrt{16} \times \sqrt{4x^2} =$ _____	10) Evaluate. $\sqrt{289} =$ _____
	11) Evaluate. $\sqrt{25b^4} =$ _____	12) Evaluate. $\sqrt{9} \times \sqrt{x^2} =$ _____

Name:	Date: ....

Topic	*Adding and Subtracting Radical Expressions*
Notes	☑ Only numbers that have the same radical part can be added or subtracted. ☑ Remember, combining "unlike" radical terms is not possible. ☑ For number with the same radical part, just add or subtract factors outside the radicals.
Example	**1) Simplify.** $6\sqrt{5} + 3\sqrt{5}$ Add like terms: $6\sqrt{5} + 3\sqrt{5} = 9\sqrt{5}$ **2) Simplify.** $5\sqrt{7} - 3\sqrt{7}$ Combine like terms: $5\sqrt{7} - 3\sqrt{7} = 2\sqrt{7}$

Your Turn!	1) **Simplify:** $\sqrt{6} + 6\sqrt{6} =$ _____	2) **Simplify:** $9\sqrt{8} - 6\sqrt{2} =$ _____
	3) **Simplify:** $-\sqrt{7} - 5\sqrt{7} =$ _____	4) **Simplify:** $10\sqrt{2} + 3\sqrt{18} =$ _____
	5) **Simplify:** $\sqrt{12} - 6\sqrt{3} =$ _____	6) **Simplify:** $-2\sqrt{x} + 6\sqrt{x} =$ _____

Name:	Date: ....

Topic	*Multiplying Radical Expressions*	
Notes	✅ To multiply radical expressions: ✅ Multiply the numbers outside of the radicals. ✅ Multiply the numbers inside the radicals. ✅ Simplify if needed.	
Example	***Evaluate.*** $\sqrt{36} \times \sqrt{4} =$ First factor the numbers: $36 = 6^2$ and $4 = 2^2$ Then: $\sqrt{36} \times \sqrt{4} = \sqrt{6^2} \times \sqrt{2^2}$ Now use radical rule: $\sqrt[n]{a^n} = a$, Then: $\sqrt{6^2} \times \sqrt{2^2} = 6 \times 2 = 12$ ***Evaluate.*** $4\sqrt{3} \times 3\sqrt{2} =$ Multiply the numbers: $4 \times 3 = 12$ $4\sqrt{3} \times 3\sqrt{2} = 12\sqrt{3}\sqrt{2}$ Use radical rule: $\sqrt{a}\sqrt{b} = \sqrt{ab} \rightarrow 12\sqrt{3}\sqrt{2} = 12\sqrt{3 \times 2} = 12\sqrt{6}$	
Your Turn!	***Evaluate:*** $\sqrt{4} \times 2\sqrt{9} =$ _____	***Evaluate:*** $\sqrt{5y} \times 3\sqrt{20y} =$ _____
	Evaluate: $-6\sqrt{4} \times 3\sqrt{4} =$ _____	***Evaluate:*** $-9\sqrt{3b^2} \times (-\sqrt{6}) =$ _____

Name:	Date: ....

Topic	*Simplifying Radical Expressions Involving Fractions*
Notes	☑ Radical expressions cannot be in the denominator. (number in the bottom) ☑ To get rid of the radical in the denominator, multiply both numerator and denominator by the radical in the denominator. ☑ If there is a radical and another integer in the denominator, multiply both numerator and denominator by the conjugate of the denominator. ☑ The conjugate of a + b is a-b and vice versa.
Example	**Simplify** $\frac{1}{\sqrt{5}-2}$ Multiply by the conjugate: $\frac{\sqrt{5}+2}{\sqrt{5}+2}$ → $\frac{1}{\sqrt{5}-2} \times \frac{\sqrt{5}+2}{\sqrt{5}+2}$ $(\sqrt{5}-2)(\sqrt{5}+2)=1$ then: $\frac{1}{\sqrt{5}-2} \times \frac{\sqrt{5}+2}{\sqrt{5}+2} = \frac{(\sqrt{5}+2)}{1} = \sqrt{5}+2$
Your Turn!	13) **Simplify:** $\frac{1+\sqrt{5}}{1-\sqrt{3}} =$ _____ 14) **Simplify:** $\frac{2+\sqrt{6}}{\sqrt{2}-\sqrt{5}} =$ _____ 15) **Simplify:** $\frac{\sqrt{7}}{\sqrt{6}-\sqrt{3}} =$ _____ 16) **Simplify:** $\frac{\sqrt{8a}}{a^5} =$ _____

Name:		Date: ....
Topic		***Radical Equations***

Notes	☑ Isolate the radical on one side of the equation. ☑ Square both sides of the equation to remove the radical ☑ Solve the equation for the variable ☑ Plugin the answer into the original equation to avoid extraneous values.
Example	Solve $\sqrt{x} - 8 = -3$ Add 8 to both sides: $\sqrt{x} = 5$ Square both sides: $(\sqrt{x})^2 = 5^2 \rightarrow x = 25$ Substitute x by 25 in the original equation and check the answer: $$x = 25 \rightarrow \sqrt{x} - 8 = \sqrt{25} - 8 = -3$$ So, the value of 2 for x is correct.

Your Turn!	1) *Solve:* $2\sqrt{2x - 4} = 8$ _____	2) *Solve:* $9 = \sqrt{4x - 1}$ _____
	3) *Solve:* $\sqrt{x} + 6 = 11$ _____	4) *Solve:* $\sqrt{5x} = \sqrt{x + 3}$ _____

Name:	Date: ....

Topic	***Domain and Range of Radical Functions***	
Notes	☑ To find the domain of the function, find all possible values of the variable inside radical. ☑ Remember that having a negative number under the square root symbol is not possible. (For cubic roots, we can have negative numbers) ☑ To find the range, plugin the minimum and maximum values of the variable inside radical.	
Example	Find the domain and range of the radical function. $$y = \sqrt{x-8} + 5$$ For domain: Find non-negative values for radicals: $x - 8 \geq 0$ Then solve for x: $x - 8 \geq 0 \rightarrow x \geq 8$ Domain: $x \geq 8$ For range: the range of a radical function of the form $c\sqrt{ax+b} + k$ is $f(x) \geq k$ $k = 5$, Then: $f(x) \geq 5$	
Your Turn!	1) **Identify the Domain and Range:** $$y = \sqrt{x+1}$$	2) **Identify the Domain and Range:** $$y = \sqrt{x-2} + 6$$
	3) **Sketch the graph of function:** $$y = 2\sqrt{x} + 1$$ 	4) **Sketch the graph of function:** $$y = \sqrt{x} + 5$$

Answers - Chapter 16

Simplifying Radical Expressions

1) 7
2) 18
3) $8x$

4) 17
5) $5b^2$
6) $3x$

Adding and Subtracting Radical Expressions

1) $7\sqrt{6}$
2) $12\sqrt{2}$
3) $-6\sqrt{7}$

4) $19\sqrt{2}$
5) $-4\sqrt{3}$
6) $4\sqrt{x}$

Multiplying Radical Expressions

1) 12
2) 30y

3) -72
4) $27b\sqrt{2}$

Simplifying Radical Expressions Involving Fractions

1) $-\frac{(1+\sqrt{5})(1+\sqrt{3})}{2}$
2) $-\frac{2\sqrt{2}+2\sqrt{5}+2\sqrt{3}+\sqrt{30}}{3}$

3) $\frac{\sqrt{7}(\sqrt{6}+\sqrt{3})}{3}$
4) $\frac{2\sqrt{2}}{a^2}$

Radical Equations

1) $x = 10$
2) $x = 20.5$

3) $x = 25$
4) $x = \frac{3}{4}$

Domain and Range of Radical Functions

1) $x \geq -1, y \geq 0$

2) $x \geq 2, y \geq 6$

3)

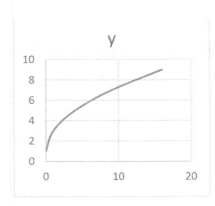

4)

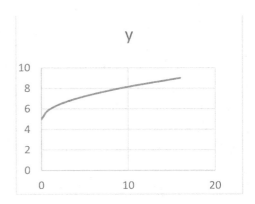

Chapter 17:

Logarithms

Math Topics that you'll learn in this Chapter:

✓ Properties of Logarithms

✓ Evaluating Logarithms

✓ Natural Logarithms

✓ Solving Logarithms Equation

Name:	Date: ....

Topic	*Properties of Logarithms*	
Notes	☑ Learn some logarithms properties:	
	$a^{\log_a b} = b$	$\log_a(x \cdot y) = \log_a x + \log_a y$
	$\log_a 1 = 0$	$\log_a \frac{x}{y} = \log_a x - \log_a y$
	$\log_a a = 1$	$\log_{x^k} x = \frac{1}{x} \log_a x , for\ k \neq 0$
	$\log_a \frac{1}{x} = -\log_a x$	$\log_a x^p = p\ \log_a x$
	$\log_a x = \frac{1}{\log_x a}$	$\log_a x = \log_{a^c} x^c$
Example	Condense this expression to a single logarithm. $$\log_b 2 - \log_b 7$$ **Solution:** Use log rule: $\log_a x - \log_a y = \log_a \frac{x}{y}$ Then: $\log_b 2 - \log_b 7 = \log_b \frac{2}{7}$	
Your Turn!	Condense this expression to a single logarithm.	
	17) $\log_a 5 - \log_a 8 =$ _____	18) $\log_x 3 - \log_x 5 =$ _____
	19) $\log_b 2 + \log_b 3 =$ _____	20) $\log_a 7 + \log_a 2 =$ _____

Name:		Date: ....

Topic	*Evaluating Logarithm*
Notes	☑Logarithm is another way of writing exponent. $log_b{}^y = x$ is equivalent to $y = b^x$. ☑Learn some logarithms rules: ($a > 0, a \neq 0, M > 0, N > 0$, and k is a real number.) Rule 1: $log_a(M.N) = log_aM + log_aN$, Rule 2: $log_a\frac{M}{N} = log_aM - log_aN$ Rule 3: $log_a(M)^k = klog_aM$, Rule 4: $log_aa = 1$, Rule 5: $log_a{}^1 = 0$ Rule 6: $a^{log_ak} = k$
Example	**Evaluate** $3log_2(8)$ **Solution:** $8 = 2^3$, then $log_2(8) = log_2(2)^3$ Use log rule: $log_a(M)^k = klog_a(M) \rightarrow log_2(2)^3 = 3log_2(2)$ Use log rule: $log_a(a) = 1 \rightarrow 3 \times 3log_2{}^2 = 3 \times 3 = 9$
Your Turn!	21) $2log_3(27) = $ _____ 22) $3log_4(256) = $ _____ 23) $\frac{1}{2}log_3(9) = $ _____ 24) $3log_5(25) = $ _____ 25) $6log_3(3) = $ _____ 26) $4log_6(1) = $ _____

Name:	Date: ....

Topic	*Natural Logarithms*	
Notes	☑ A natural logarithm is a logarithm that has a special base of the mathematical constant e, which is an irrational number approximately equal to 2.71. ☑ The natural logarithm of x is generally written as $ln\,x$, or $log_e\,x$.	
Example	**Solve this equation for** x: $ln(3x - 4) = 1$ **Solution:** Use *log* rule: $a = log_b(b^a) \rightarrow 1 = ln(e^1) = ln(e) \rightarrow$ $ln(3x - 4) = ln\,(e)$ When the logs have the same base: $log_b(f(x)) = log_b(g(x)) \rightarrow$ $f(x) = g(x)$ $ln(3x - 4) = ln(e)$, then: $3x - 4 = e \rightarrow x = \frac{e+4}{3}$	
Your Turn!	1) *Solve for x:* $e^x = 36$, $x =$ _____	2) *Solve for x:* $ln\,x = 5$, $x =$ _____
	3) *Solve for x:* $ln(2x - 3) = 1$, $x =$ _____	4) *Solve for x:* $ln(ln\,x) = 2$, $x =$ _____
	5) *Reduce this expressions to simplest form:* $e^{ln\left(\frac{6}{e}\right)} =$ _____	6) *Reduce this expressions to simplest form:* $ln(\frac{1}{e})^3 =$ _____

Name:	Date: ....

Topic	*Solving Logarithmic Equations*	
Notes	☑ Convert the logarithmic equation to an exponential equation when it's possible. (If no base is indicated, the base of the logarithm is 10) ☑ Condense logarithms if you have more than one log on one side of the equation. ☑ Plug in the answers back into the original equation and check to see if the solution works.	
Example	*Find the value of the variables in this equation.* $$log_2(25 - x^2) = 4$$ **Solution:** Use the logarithmic definition: $log_a(b) = c \rightarrow a^c = b$ $$log_2(25 - x^2) = 4 \rightarrow 2^4 = (25 - x^2) \rightarrow 16 = (25 - x^2)$$ Simplify: $16 = (25 - x^2) \rightarrow -x^2 + 25 - 16 = 0$ Then: $x^2 = 9 \rightarrow x = 3 \; or -3$ Both 3 and -3 work in the original equation.	
Your Turn!	1) *Find the value of x:* $log_3 4x = 0 , x = $ _____	2) *Find the value of x:* $log x + 4 = 1 , x = $ _____
	3) *Find the value of x:* $log 3 - log x = 0 , x = $ ____	4) *Find the value of x:* $log(x - 3) - log 6 = 0 , x = $ ____

Answers - Chapter 17

Properties of Logarithms

1) $log_a \frac{5}{8}$

2) $log_x \frac{3}{5}$

3) $log_b(6)$

4) $log_a(14)$

Evaluating Logarithm

1) 6

2) 12

3) 1

4) 6

5) 6

6) 0

Natural Logarithms

1) $2ln6$

2) e^5

3) $\frac{e+3}{2}$

4) e^{e^2}

5) $\frac{6}{e}$

6) -3

Solving Logarithmic Equations

1) $\frac{1}{4}$

2) $\frac{1}{1000}$

3) 3

4) 9

Chapter 18:

Circles

Topics that you'll practice in this chapter:

- ✓ Circumference and Area of circle

- ✓ Arc Length and Sector Area

- ✓ Equation of a Circle

- ✓ Finding the Center and the Radius of Circles

Name:	Date: ....

Topic	**Circumference and Area of Circles**
Notes	✓ In a circle, variable r is usually used for the radius and d for diameter and π is about 3.14. ✓ $Area\ of\ a\ circle = \pi r^2$ ✓ $Circumference\ of\ a\ circle = 2\pi r$

Example	**Find the area of the circle.**
	  Solution:
	  Use area formula: $Area = \pi r^2$
	  $r = 2\ in \rightarrow Area = \pi(2)^2 = 4\pi, \pi = 3.14$
	  Then: $Area = 4 \times 3.14 = 12.56\ in^2$

	Find the area of each circle. $(\pi = 3.14)$
Your Turn!	1) _____	2) _____
	Find the Circumference of each circle. $(\pi = 3.14)$
	3) _____	4) _____

Name: ....   Date: ....

Topic	*Arc Length and Sector Area*
Notes	✓ To find the area of a sector of a circle, use this formula: Area of a sector $= \pi r^2(\frac{\theta}{360})$, r is the radius of the circle and θ is the central angle of the sector. ✓ To find the arc of a sector of a circle, use this formula: Arc of a sector $= (\frac{\theta}{180})\pi r$
Example	**1) Find the length of the arc. Round your answer to the nearest tenth.** $(\pi = 3.14)$, $r = 8\ cm$, $\theta = 30°$ **Solution:** Use this formula: length of a sector$= (\frac{\theta}{180})\pi r$ Length of a sector$= \left(\frac{30}{180}\right)\pi(8) = \left(\frac{1}{6}\right)\pi(8) = 1.3 \times 3.14 \cong 4.2\ cm$ **2) Find the area of the sector.** $r = 4\ ft, \theta = 80°$ **Solution:** Use this formula: Area of a sector$= \pi r^2(\frac{\theta}{360})$ Area of a sector $= \pi r^2\left(\frac{\theta}{360}\right) = (3.14)(4^2)\left(\frac{80}{360}\right) \cong 11.2$

Your Turn!	*Find the length of the arc.*
	
	1) $r = 12\ ft, \theta = 120°$ 2) $r = 8\ cm, \theta = 32°$
	
	    Length of the arc: _____ *Length of the arc: _____*
	
	Find the area of the sector.
	
	3) 4)
	
	     16in $\frac{16\pi}{7}$ 12 ft
	     320°
	
	Area of the sector: _____ *Area of the sector: _____*

Name:	Date: ....

Topic	*Equation of a Circle*
Notes	☑ Equation of circles in standard form: $(x-h)^2 + (y-k)^2 = r^2$, Center: (h, k), Radius: r ☑ General format: $x^2 + y^2 + Ax + By + C = 0$
Example	***Write the standard form equation of this circle.*** $$x^2 + y^2 + 6x - 10y - 7 = 0$$ **Solution:** $(x-h)^2 + (y-k)^2 = r^2$ is the circle equation with a radius r, centered at (h, k). To find this equation, first, move the loose number to the right side: $x^2 + y^2 + 6x - 10y = 7$ Group x-variables and y-variables together: $(x^2 + 6x) + (y^2 - 10y) = 7$ Convert x to square form: $(x^2 + 6x + 9) + (y^2 - 10y) = 7 + 9 \rightarrow (x+3)^2 + (y^2 - 10y) = 7 + 9 \rightarrow$ Convert y to square form: $(x+3)^2 + (y^2 - 10y + 25) = 7 + 9 + 25 \rightarrow (x+3)^2 + (y-5)^2 = 36$ Then: $(x - (-3))^2 + (y-5)^2 = 6^2$

Write the standard form equation of each circle.

Your Turn!	*1)* $x^2 + y^2 - 8x + 8y + 7 = 0$ Standard form: _____	*2)* $x^2 + y^2 - 4x + 10y + 13 = 0$ Standard form: _____
	3) Center: $(-1, -2)$, Radius: 2 Standard form: _____	*4)* Center: $(-4, -1)$, Area: 4π Standard form: _____

| Name: .... | | Date: .... |

Topic	*Finding the Center and the Radius of Circles*	
Notes	To find the center and the radius of a circle using the equation of the circle: ☑ Write the equation of the circle in standard form: $(x - h)^2 + (y - k)^2 = r^2$, ☑ The center of the circle is at (h, k), and its radius is r.	

Example

Identify the center and radius. $8x + x^2 - 2y = 8 - y^2$

Solution: $(x - h)^2 + (y - k)^2 = r^2$ is the circle equation with a radius r, centered at (h, k).

Rewrite $8x + x^2 - 2y = 8 - y^2$ in the standard form:

$$(x - (-4))^2 + (y - 1)^2 = 5^2$$

Then, the center is at $(-4, 1)$ and $r = 5$

Your Turn!

Identify the center and radius of each circle.

1) $(x - 2)^2 + (y + 6)^2 = 16$ Center: (___,___) Radius: _____	2) $(x + 9)^2 + (y + 3)^2 = 20$ Center: (___,___) Radius: _____
3) $x^2 + y^2 + 12y = 3 + 10x$ Center: (___,___) Radius: _____	4) $x^2 - 8x + 16y = 1 - y^2$ Center: (___,___) Radius: _____

Answers - Chapter 18

Circumference and Area of Circles

1) $113.04\ cm^2$

2) $314\ in^2$

3) $50.24\ cm$

4) $37.68\ m$

Arc Length and Sector Area

1) $25.12\ cm$

2) $4.47\ cm$

3) $714.5\ in^2$

4) $387.6\ ft^2$

Equation of a Circle

1) $(x-4)^2 + \left(y-(-4)\right)^2 = 5^2$

2) $(x-2)^2 + \left(y-(-5)\right)^2 = 4^2$

3) $\left(x-(-1)\right)^2 + \left(y-(-2)\right)^2 = 2^2$

4) $(x-(-4))^2 + (y-(-1))^2 = 2^2$

Finding the Center and the Radius of Circles

1) Center: $(2,-6)$ Radius: 4

2) Center: $(-9,-3)$ Radius: $\sqrt{20}$

3) Center: $(5,-6)$ Radius: 8

4) Center: $(4,-8)$ Radius: 9

Chapter 19:

Rational Expressions

Math Topics that you'll learn in this Chapter:

✓ Simplifying Complex Fractions

✓ Graphing Rational Functions

✓ Adding and Subtracting Rational Expressions

✓ Multiplying Rational Expressions

✓ Dividing Rational expressions

✓ Rational Equations

Name:	Date: ....

Topic	*Simplify Complex Fractions*
Notes	☑ Convert mixed numbers to improper fractions. ☑ Simplify all fractions. ☑ Write the fraction in the numerator of the main fraction line then write division sing (÷) and the fraction of the denominator. ☑ Use normal method for dividing fractions. ☑ Simplify as needed.
Example	Solve: $\dfrac{\frac{2}{3}}{\frac{7}{10}-\frac{1}{4}}$ **Solution:** First, simplify the denominator: $\frac{7}{10}-\frac{1}{4}=\frac{9}{2-}$, Then: $\dfrac{\frac{2}{3}}{\frac{7}{10}-\frac{1}{4}}=\dfrac{\frac{2}{3}}{\frac{9}{20}}$ Now, write the complex fraction using the division sign (÷): $\dfrac{\frac{2}{3}}{\frac{9}{20}}=\frac{2}{3}\div\frac{9}{20}$ Use the dividing fractions rule: Keep, Change, Flip (keep the first fraction, change the division sign to multiplication, flip the second fraction) $$\frac{2}{3}\div\frac{9}{20}=\frac{2}{3}\times\frac{20}{9}=\frac{40}{27}=1\frac{13}{27}$$
Your Turn!	1) $\dfrac{\frac{8}{3}}{\frac{2}{5}}=$ _____ 2) $\dfrac{\frac{x}{3}+\frac{x}{8}}{\frac{1}{4}}=$ _____ 3) $\dfrac{\frac{x+3}{3}}{\frac{x-2}{2}}=$ _____ 4) $\dfrac{1+\frac{x}{4}}{x}=$ _____

Name:	Date: ....

Topic	*Graphing Rational Expressions*
Notes	☑ Find the vertical asymptotes of the function, if there is any. (Vertical asymptotes are vertical lines which correspond to the zeroes of the denominator) ☑ Find horizontal or slant asymptote. (If numerator has a bigger degree than denominator, there will be slant asymptote.) ☑ If denominator has a bigger degree than numerator, the horizontal asymptote is the x-axes or the line $y = 0$. If they have the same degree, the horizontal asymptote equals the leading coefficient (the coefficient of the largest exponent) of the numerator divided by the leading coefficient of the denominator. ☑ Find intercepts and plug in some values of x and solve for y and graph.

Example	*Graph rational expressions.* $f(x) = \frac{3x}{x^2-2x}$ **Solution:** First, notice that the graph is in two pieces. Find $y - intercept$ by substituting zero for x and solving for y ($f(x)$): $x = 0 \rightarrow$ $y = \frac{3x}{x^2-2x} = \frac{3(0)}{0^2-2(0)} = \frac{0}{0}, y -$ $intercept: None$ Asymptotes of $\frac{3x}{x^2-2x}$: vertical: $x = 2$, Horizontal: $y = 0$ After finding the asymptotes, you can plug in some values for x and solve for y. Here is the sketch for this function.

Your Turn!	1) *Graph rational expressions.* $f(x) = \frac{x^2-2x}{x-3}$	2) *Graph rational expressions.* $f(x) = \frac{6x+1}{x^2-4x}$

Name:	Date: ....

Topic	***Adding and Subtracting Rational Expressions***	
Notes	For adding and subtracting rational expressions: ☑ Find least common denominator (LCD). ☑ Write each expression using the LCD. ☑ Add or subtract the numerators. ☑ Simplify as needed.	
Examples	**1) Solve.** $\frac{3}{x+4} + \frac{x-2}{x+4} =$ Use fraction addition rule: $\frac{a}{c} \pm \frac{b}{c} = \frac{a \pm b}{c} \rightarrow \frac{3}{x+4} + \frac{x-2}{x+4} = \frac{3+(x-2)}{x+4} =$ $\frac{x+1}{x+4}$ **2) Solve.** $\frac{x+4}{x-8} + \frac{x}{x+6} =$ Least common denominator of $(x-8)$ and $(x+6)$: $(x-8)(x+6)$ Then: $\frac{(x+4)(x+6)}{(x-8)(x+6)} + \frac{x(x-8)}{(x+6)(x-8)} = \frac{(x+4)(x+6)+x(x-8)}{(x+6)(x-6)}$ Expand: $(x+4)(x+6) + x(x-8) = 2x^2 + 2x + 24$ Then: $\frac{x+4}{x-8} + \frac{x}{x+6} = \frac{2x^2+2x+24}{(x+6)(x-8)}$	
Your Turn!	1) $\frac{x+6}{x+1} - \frac{x+9}{x+1} =$ _____	2) $\frac{2x+1}{x+3} + \frac{2}{x+4} =$ _____
	3) $\frac{14}{x+4} + \frac{6}{x^2-16} =$ _____	4) $\frac{x+2}{x+8} - \frac{2x}{x-8} =$ _____

Name:		Date: ....

Topic	*Multiplying Rational Expressions*	
Notes	☑ Multiplying rational expressions is the same as multiplying fractions. First, multiply numerators and then multiply denominators. Then, simplify as needed.	
Examples	1) Solve: $\frac{x+5}{x-1} \times \frac{x-1}{3} =$ Multiply fractions: $\frac{x+5}{x-1} \times \frac{x-1}{3} = \frac{(x+5)(x-1)}{3(x-1)}$ Cancel the common factor: $(x-1)$, then: $\frac{(x+5)(x-1)}{3(x-1)} = \frac{(x+5)}{3}$ 2) Solve $\frac{x-5}{x+4} \times \frac{2x+8}{x-5} =$ Multiply fractions: $\frac{x-5}{x+4} \times \frac{2x+8}{x-5} = \frac{(x-5)(2x+8)}{(x+4)(x-5)}$ Cancel the common factor: $\frac{(x-5)(2x+8)}{(x+4)(x-5)} = \frac{(2x+8)}{(x+4)}$ Factor $2x+8 = 2(x+4)$, Then: $\frac{2(x+4)}{(x+4)} = 2$	
Your Turn!	1) $\frac{20x^3}{3} \times \frac{15}{4x} =$ _____	2) $\frac{x+6}{4} \times \frac{16}{x+6} =$ _____
	3) $\frac{x+10}{4x} \times \frac{3x}{7x+70} =$ _____	4) $\frac{x+8}{x+6} \times \frac{x-6}{4x+32} =$ _____

Name: .... Date: ....

Topic	*Dividing Rational Expressions*
Notes	☑ To divide rational expression, use the same method we use for dividing fractions. ☑ Keep, Change, Flip ☑ Keep first rational expression, change division sign to multiplication, and flip the numerator and denominator of the second rational expression. Then, multiply numerators and multiply denominators. Simplify as needed.
Example	**Solve** $\dfrac{2x}{5} \div \dfrac{8}{7} =$ $\dfrac{2x}{5} \div \dfrac{8}{7} = \dfrac{\frac{2x}{5}}{\frac{8}{7}}$, Use Divide fractions rules: $\dfrac{\frac{a}{b}}{\frac{c}{d}} = \dfrac{a\cdot d}{b\cdot c}$ $\dfrac{\frac{2x}{5}}{\frac{8}{7}} = \dfrac{2x\times7}{8\times5} = \dfrac{14x}{40} = \dfrac{7x}{20}$ **Solve** $\dfrac{6x}{x+2} \div \dfrac{x}{6x+12} =$ $\dfrac{\frac{6x}{x+2}}{\frac{x}{6x+12}}$, Use Divide fractions rules: $\dfrac{(6x)(6x+12)}{(x)(x+2)}$ Cancel common fraction: $\dfrac{(6x)(6x+12)}{(x)(x+2)} = \dfrac{36(x+2)}{(x+2)} = 36$
Your Turn!	1) $\dfrac{10x}{x+2} \div \dfrac{x}{60x+120} =$ _____ 2) $\dfrac{5}{4} \div \dfrac{45}{8x} =$ _____ 3) $\dfrac{x-6}{x+3} \div \dfrac{4}{x+3} =$ _____ 4) $\dfrac{7x^3}{x^2-64} \div \dfrac{x^3}{x^2+x-56} =$ _____

Name:	Date: ....

Topic	Rational Equations
Notes	For solving rational equations, we can use following methods: ☑ Converting to a common denominator: In this method, you need to get a common denominator for both sides of the equation. Then make the numerators equal and solve for the variable. ☑ Cross-multiplying: This method is useful when there is only one fraction on each side of the equation. Simply multiply the first numerator by the second denominator and make the result equal to the product of the second numerator and the first denominator.

Example	Solve. $\dfrac{x-3}{x+1} = \dfrac{x+5}{x-2}$ Use cross multiply method: if $\dfrac{a}{b} = \dfrac{c}{d}$, then: $a \times d = b \times c$ Then: $(x-3)(x-2) = (x+5)(x+1)$ Expand: $(x-3)(x-2) = x^2 - 5x + 6$ Expand: $(x+5)(x+1) = x^2 + 6x + 5$, Then: $x^2 - 5x + 6 = x^2 + 6x + 5$, Simplify: $x^2 - 5x = x^2 + 6x - 1$ Subtract both sides $x^2 + 6x$,Then: $-11x = -1 \rightarrow x = \dfrac{1}{11}$

Your Turn!	5) $\dfrac{1}{x^2} + \dfrac{4}{x} = \dfrac{6}{x}$ $x = $ ___	6) $\dfrac{2}{x^2} - \dfrac{1}{x} = 1$ $x = $ ___
	7) $\dfrac{x+1}{5x} - 1 = \dfrac{1}{x}$ $x = $ ___	8) $\dfrac{6}{x} - \dfrac{1}{x} = \dfrac{1}{x^2+6x}$ $x = $ ___

Answers - Chapter 19

Simplify Complex Fractions

1) $\frac{20}{3}$

2) $\frac{11x}{6}$

3) $\frac{2x+6}{3x-6}$

4) $\frac{4+x}{4x}$

Graphing Rational Expressions

1)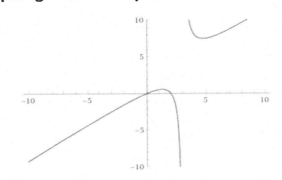

2)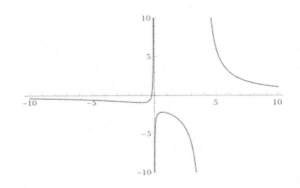

Adding and Subtracting Rational Expressions

1) $-\frac{3}{x+1}$

2) $\frac{2x^2+11x+1}{(x+3)(x+4)}$

3) $\frac{14x-5}{(x+4)(x-4)}$

4) $\frac{-x^2-22x}{(x+8)(x-8)}$

Multiplying Rational Expressions

1) $25x^2$

2) 4

3) $\frac{3}{28}$

4) $\frac{x-6}{4(x+6)}$

Dividing Rational Expressions

1) 600

2) $\frac{2x}{9}$

3) $\frac{x-6}{4}$

4) $\frac{7(x-7)}{x-8}$

Rational Equations

1) $x = \frac{1}{2}$

2) $x = 1$ or $x = -2$

3) $x = -1$

4) $x = -\frac{29}{5}$

Chapter 20:

Trigonometric Functions

Topics that you'll practice in this chapter:

✓ Trigonometric Functions

✓ Co–Terminal Angles and Reference Angles

✓ Evaluating Trigonometric Function

✓ Missing Sides and Angles of a Right Triangle

✓ Angle and Angle Measure

Name: ....

Date: ....

Topic	*Trigonometric Functions*				

Notes						

✓ Learn common trigonometric functions:

θ	0°	30°	45°	60°	90°
$\sin\theta$	0	$\dfrac{1}{2}$	$\dfrac{\sqrt{2}}{2}$	$\dfrac{\sqrt{3}}{2}$	1
$\cos\theta$	1	$\dfrac{\sqrt{3}}{2}$	$\dfrac{\sqrt{2}}{2}$	$\dfrac{1}{2}$	0
$\tan\theta$	0	$\dfrac{\sqrt{3}}{3}$	1	$\sqrt{3}$	Undefined

Example

Find $\sin 135°$.

Solution: Use the following property: $sin(x) = cos(90° - x)$

$sin\, 135° = cos(90° - 135°) = cos(-45°)$

Now use the following property: $cos(-x) = \cos(x)$

$cos(-45°) = cos(45°) = \dfrac{\sqrt{2}}{2}$

Your Turn!

1) $sin\,(30°) = $ _____

2) $cot\,(30°) = $ _____

3) $sin(-90°) = $ _____

4) $\cos\,(-60°) = $ _____

5) $tan(-120°) = $ _____

6) $sec\,(480°) = $ _____

| Name: .... | Date: .... |

Topic	*Co-terminal Angles and Reference Angles*
Notes	✓ Co-terminal angles are equal angles. ✓ To find a Co-terminal of an angle, add or subtract 360 degrees (or 2π for radians) to the given angle. ✓ Reference angle is the smallest angle that you can make from the terminal side of an angle with the x-axis.
Example	Find a positive and a negative Co-terminal angles to angle 95°. **Solution:** $95° - 360° = -265°$ $95° + 360° = 455°$ $-265°$ and a $455°$ are Co-terminal with a $95°$.

Your Turn!

Find a positive and a negative Co-terminal angles.

1) $80° =$ Positive = _____ Negative =_____	2) $120° =$ Positive = _____ Negative =_____
3) $-115° =$ Positive = _____ Negative =_____	4) $\frac{\pi}{5} =$ Positive = _____ Negative =_____
5) $\frac{3\pi}{4} =$ Positive = _____ Negative =_____	6) $\frac{2\pi}{7} =$ Positive = _____ Negative =_____

Name:	Date: ....

Topic	*Evaluating Trigonometric Function*
Notes	✓ Step 1: Find the reference angle. (It is the smallest angle that you can make from the terminal side of an angle with the x-axis.) ✓ Step 2: Determine the quadrant of the function. Depending on the quadrant in which the function lies, the answer will be either be positive or negative. ✓ Step 3: Find the trigonometric function of the reference angle.
Example	*Find the exact value of trigonometric function.* $tan\,\frac{7\pi}{6}$ **Solution:** Rewrite the angles for $an\,\frac{4\pi}{3}$: $tan\,\frac{4\pi}{3} = tan\left(\frac{3\pi+\pi}{3}\right) = \tan\left(\pi + \frac{1}{3}\pi\right)$. Use the periodicity of tan: $tan(x + \pi.k) = tan(x)$. Recall that $\tan\frac{1}{3}\pi = \sqrt{3}$ Then: $tan\left(\pi + \frac{1}{3}\pi\right) = ta\,n\left(\frac{1}{3}\pi\right) = \sqrt{3}$
Your Turn!	1) $cot\,150° =$ _____ 2) $sin\,120° =$ _____ 3) $tan\,300° =$ _____ 4) $cot\,\frac{5\pi}{3} =$ _____ 5) $cos\,\frac{11\pi}{6} =$ _____ 6) $csc\,\frac{5\pi}{6} =$ _____

Name: ....

Date: ....

Topic	*Missing Sides and Angles of a Right Triangle*
Notes	✓ By using Sine, Cosine or Tangent, we can find an unknown side in a right triangle when we have one length, and one angle (apart from the right angle). ✓ Adjacent, Opposite and Hypotenuse, in a right triangle is shown below. ✓ ✓ Recall the three main trigonometric functions: SOH − CAH − TOA $sin\ \theta = \frac{opposite}{hypotenuse}, Cos\ \theta = \frac{adjacent}{hypotenuse}, \tan\theta = \frac{opposite}{adjacent}$ ✓ To find missing angles, use inverse of trigonometric functions (examples: $sin^{-1}, cos^{-1}, and\ tan^{-1}$)
Example	Find side AC in the following triangle. Round answers to the nearest tenth. **Solution:** $sin\ \theta = \frac{opposite}{hypotenus}. \ sine\ 35° = \frac{AC}{8} \rightarrow 8 \times sin\ 35° = AC,$ Now use a calculator to find $sin\ 35°$. $sin\ 35° \approx 0.574, AC = 8 \times 0.574 = 4.59$
Your Turn!	1) _____ 45° 10 x 2) _____ 15 x° 5 3) _____ 60° x 6 4) _____ 12 x° 8

Name:	Date: ....

Topic	Angle and Angle Measure
Notes	✓ To convert degrees to radians, use this formula: $$\text{Radians} = \text{Degrees} \times \frac{\pi}{180}$$ ✓ To convert radians to degrees, use this formula: $$\text{Degrees} = \text{Radians} \times \frac{180}{\pi}$$
Examples	**1) Convert 140 degrees to radians.** **Solution:** Use this formula: $\text{Radians} = \text{Degrees} \times \frac{\pi}{180}$ $\text{Radian} = 140 \times \frac{\pi}{180} = \frac{140\pi}{180} = \frac{7}{9}\pi$ **2) Convert $\frac{9}{5}\pi$ to degrees.** **Solution:** Use this formula: $\text{Degrees} = \text{Radians} \times \frac{180}{\pi}$ $\text{Degree} = \frac{9\pi}{5} \times \frac{180}{\pi} = \frac{1620\pi}{5\pi} = 324^\circ$
Your Turn!	*Convert each degree measure into radians.*

1) $50^\circ =$	2) $-110^\circ =$

Convert each radian measure into degrees.

3) $\frac{\pi}{5} =$	4) $-\frac{3\pi}{2} =$

Answers - Chapter 20

Trigonometric Functions

1) $\frac{1}{2}$
2) $\sqrt{3}$
3) -1

4) $\frac{1}{2}$
5) $\sqrt{3}$
6) -2

Co-terminal Angles and Reference Angles

1) Positive $= 440°$, Negative $= -280°$
2) Positive $= 480°$, Negative $= -240°$
3) Positive $= 245°$, Negative $= -475°$
4) Positive $= \frac{11\pi}{5}$, Negative $= -\frac{9\pi}{5}$
5) Positive $= \frac{11\pi}{4}$, Negative $= -\frac{5\pi}{4}$
6) Positive $= \frac{16}{7}$, Negative $= -\frac{12\pi}{7}$

Evaluating Trigonometric Function

1) $-\sqrt{3}$
2) $\frac{\sqrt{3}}{2}$
3) $-\sqrt{3}$

4) $-\frac{\sqrt{3}}{2}$
5) $\frac{\sqrt{3}}{2}$
6) 2

Missing Sides and Angles of a Right Triangle

1) 7
2) 18

3) 6.93
4) 56°

Angle and Angle Measure

1) $\frac{5}{18}\pi$
2) $-\frac{11}{18}\pi$

3) $36°$
4) $-270°$

ALEKS Test Review

ALEKS (Assessment and Learning in Knowledge Spaces) is an artificial intelligence-based assessment tool to measure the strengths and weaknesses of a student's mathematical knowledge. ALEKS is available for a variety of subjects and courses in K-12, Higher Education, and Continuing Education. The findings of ALEKS's assessment test help to find an appropriate level for course placement. The ALEKS math placement assessment ensures students' readiness for particular math courses at colleges.

ALEKS does not use multiple-choice questions like most other standardized tests. Instead, it utilizes adaptable and easy-to-use method that mimic paper and pencil techniques. When taking the ALEKS test, a brief tutorial helps you learn how to use ALEKS answer input tools. You then begin the ALEKS Assessment. In about 30 to 45 minutes, the test measures your current content knowledge by asking 20 to 30 questions. ALEKS is a Computer Adaptive (CA) assessment. It means that each question will be chosen on the basis of answers to all the previous questions. Therefore, each set of assessment questions is unique. The ALEKS Math assessment does not allow you to use a personal calculator. But for some questions ALEKS onscreen calculator button is active and the test taker can use it.

The ALEKS Math score is between 1 and 100 and is interpreted as a percentage correct. A higher ALEKS score indicates that the test-taker has mastered more math concepts. ALEKS Math assessment tool evaluates mastery of a comprehensive set of mathematics skills ranging from basic arithmetic up to precalculus, including trigonometry but not calculus. It will place students in classes up to Calculus.

Key Features of the ALEKS Mathematics Assessment

Some key features of the ALEKS Math assessment are:

- Mathematics questions on ALEKS are adaptive to identify the student's knowledge from a comprehensive standard curriculum, ranging from basic arithmetic up to precalculus, including trigonometry but not calculus.
- Unlike other standardized tests, the ALEKS assessment does not provide a "grade" or "raw score." Instead, ALEKS identifies which concepts the student has mastered and what topics the student needs to learn.
- ALEKS does not use multiple-choice questions. Instead, students need to produce authentic mathematical input.

There is no time limit for taking the ALEKS Math assessment. But it usually takes 30 to 45

minutes to complete the assessment.

Topics covered on ALEKS Math Assessment:

- Real Numbers and Integers
- Proportions, Ratios, and Percent
- Algebraic Expressions
- Equations and Inequalities
- Linear Functions
- Exponents
- Polynomials
- Functions Operations
- Quadratic
- Radical Expressions
- Geometry and Solid Figures
- Statistics and Probability
- Complex Numbers
- Exponentials and logarithms
- Trigonometric Functions

In this section, there are 2 complete ALEKS Mathematics Tests. Take these tests to see what score you'll be able to receive on a real ALEKS test.

Good luck!

Time to Test

Time to refine your skill with a practice examination

Take a REAL ALEKS Mathematics test to simulate the test day experience. After you've finished, score your test using the answers and explanations section.

Before You Start

-   You'll need a pencil and scratch papers to take the test.

-   For these practice tests, don't time yourself. Spend time as much as you need.

-   After you've finished the test, review the answer key to see where you went wrong.

Good Luck!

ALEKS Mathematics Practice Test 1

2020 - 2021

Total number of questions: 30

Total time (Calculator): No time limit

Calculators are permitted for ALEKS Math Test.

(On a real ALEKS test, there is an onscreen calculator to use.)

1) If $f(x) = 3x - 1$ and $g(x) = x^2 - x$, then find $(\frac{f}{g})(x)$.

2) A bank is offering 3.5% simple interest on a savings account. If you deposit \$12,000, how much interest will you earn in two years?

3) If the ratio of home fans to visiting fans in a crowd is $3:2$ and all 25,000 seats in a stadium are filled, how many visiting fans are in attendance?

4) If the interior angles of a quadrilateral are in the ratio $1:2:3:4$, what is the measure of the largest angle?

5) If the area of a circle is 64 square meters, what is its diameter?

6) The length of a rectangle is $\frac{5}{4}$ times its width. If the width is 16, what is the perimeter of this rectangle?

7) In the figure below, line A is parallel to line B. What is the value of angle x?

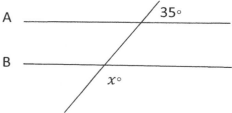

A —————————— $35°$

B ——————————

$x°$

8) An angle is equal to one fifth of its supplement. What is the measure of that angle?

9) What is the value of x in the following system of equations?

$$2x + 5y = 11$$
$$4x - 2y = -14$$

10) Last week 24,000 fans attended a football match. This week three times as many bought tickets, but one sixth of them cancelled their tickets. How many are attending this week?

11) If $sin\ A = \frac{1}{4}$ in a right triangle and the angle A is an acute angle, then what is $cos\ A$?

12) In the standard (x, y) coordinate system plane, what is the area of the circle with the following equation?

$$(x + 2)^2 + (y - 4)^2 = 16$$

13) Convert 670,000 to scientific notation.

14) The ratio of boys to girls in a school is $2:3$. If there are 600 students in a school, how many boys are in the school.

15) If 150% of a number is 75, then what is 90% of that number?

16) If $A = \begin{bmatrix} -1 & 2 \\ 1 & -2 \end{bmatrix}$ and $B = \begin{bmatrix} 4 & 1 \\ -2 & 3 \end{bmatrix}$, then $2A - B =$

17) What is the solution of the following inequality?

$$|x - 2| \geq 3$$

18) If $\tan x = \frac{8}{15}$, then $\sin x =$

19) $(x^6)^{\frac{5}{8}}$ equal to?

20) What are the zeroes of the function $f(x) = x^3 + 6x^2 + 8x$?

21) If $x + sin^2a + cos^2a = 3$, then x = ?

22) If $\sqrt{6x} = \sqrt{y}$, then $x =$

23) The average weight of 18 girls in a class is $60\ kg$ and the average weight of 32 boys in the same class is $62\ kg$. What is the average weight of all the 50 students in that class?

24) What is the value of the expression $5(x - 2y) + (2 - x)^2$ when $x = 3$ and $= -2$?

25) Sophia purchased a sofa for \$530.40. The sofa is regularly priced at \$624. What was the percent discount Sophia received on the sofa?

26) If one angle of a right triangle measures 60°, what is the sine of the other acute angle?

27) Simplify $\dfrac{5-3i}{-5i}$?

28) The average of five consecutive numbers is 38. What is the smallest number?

29) What is the slope of a line that is perpendicular to the line

$$4x - 2y = 12?$$

30) If $f(x) = 2x^4 + 2$ and $g(x) = \dfrac{1}{x}$, what is the value of $f(g(x))$?

This is the end of Practice Test 1.

ALEKS Mathematics Practice Test 2

2020 - 2021

Total number of questions: 30

Total time (Calculator): No time limit

Calculators are permitted for ALEKS Math Test.

(On a real ALEKS test, there is an onscreen calculator to use.)

1) $(x - 5)(x^2 + 5x + 4) = ?$

2) $5 + 8 \times (-3) - [4 + 22 \times 5] \div 6 = ?$

3) Simplify. $\dfrac{\dfrac{1}{2} - \dfrac{x+5}{4}}{\dfrac{x^2}{2} - \dfrac{5}{2}}$

4) How many 4×2 squares can fit inside a rectangle with a height of 52 and width of 12?

5) If $5 + 2x \leq 15$, what is the value of $x \leq$?

6) A man owed $4,265 on his car. After making 55 payments of $66 each, how much did he have left to pay?

7) $(x^4)^{\frac{5}{8}} =$

8) What is 2531.58245 rounded to the nearest tenth?

9) 25 is what percent of 75?

10) Last Friday Jacob had $34.52. Over the weekend he received some money for cleaning the attic. He now has $44. How much money did he receive?

11) In the following triangle what is the value of x?

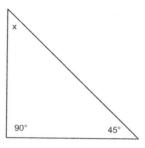

12) Find the factors of $x^2 - 7x + 12$.

13) A ladder leans against a wall forming a $60°$ angle between the ground and the ladder. If the bottom of the ladder is 30 feet away from the wall, how long is the ladder?

14) What is the distance between the points $(1, 3)$ and $(-2, 7)$?

15) Write the $\frac{2}{140}$ as a decimal. (round your answer to the nearest ten thousandths)

16) Liam's average (arithmetic mean) on two mathematics tests is 9. What should Liam's score be on the next test to have an overall of 10 for all the tests?

17) Find all values of x in this equation: $4x^2 + 14x + 6 = 0$

18) What is the value of x in this equation? $7^5 \times 7^8 = 7^x$

19) If a vehicle is driven 33 miles on Monday, 36 miles on Tuesday, and 30 miles on Wednesday, what is the average number of miles driven each day?

20) Find the solutions of the following equation.

$$x^2 + 2x - 5 = 0$$

21) What is the solution of the following system of equations?

$$\begin{cases} -2x - y = -9 \\ 5x - 2y = 9 \end{cases}$$

22) Solve. $|9 - (12 \div |2 - 6|)| = ?$

23) If $\log_2 x = 5$, then $x = ?$

24) What's the reciprocal of $\dfrac{x^3}{14}$?

25) What is the equivalent temperature of $140°F$ in Celsius?

$$C = \frac{5}{9}(F - 32)$$

26) Simplify $(-3 + 9i)(3 + 5i)$.

27) Find $tan \ \frac{2\pi}{3}$

28) If $f(x) = 5x - 1$ and $g(x) = x^2 - x$, then find $(\frac{f}{g})(x)$.

29) What is the center and radius of a circle with the following equation?
$$(x - 4)^2 + (y + 7)^2 = 3$$

30) If the center of a circle is at the point $(-4, 2)$ and its circumference equals to 2π, what is the standard form equation of the circle?

This is the end of Practice Test 2.

ALEKS Mathematics Practice Tests Answers and Explanations

Now, it's time to review your results to see where you went wrong and what areas you need to improve!

ALEKS Mathematics Practice Test 1

1) **The answer is** $\frac{3x-1}{x^2-x}$

$$\left(\frac{f}{g}\right)(x) = \frac{f(x)}{g(x)} = \frac{3x-1}{x^2-x}$$

2) **The answer is 840**

Use simple interest formula: $I = prt$ (I = interest, p = principal, r = rate, t = time)

$I = (12,000)(0.035)(2) = 840$

3) **The answer is 10,000**

Number of visiting fans: $\frac{2 \times 25,000}{5} = 10,000$

4) **The answer is $144°$**

The sum of all angles in a quadrilateral is 360 degrees. Let x be the smallest angle in the quadrilateral. Then the angles are: $x, 2x, 3x, 4x$, $x + 2x + 3x + 4x = 360 \rightarrow 10x = 360 \rightarrow x = 36$, The angles in the quadrilateral are: $36°, 72°, 108°$, and $144°$

5) **The answer is** $\frac{8\sqrt{\pi}}{\pi}$

Formula for the area of a circle is: $A = \pi r^2$, Using 64 for the area of the circle we have: $64 = \pi r^2$. Let's solve for the radius (r). $\frac{64}{\pi} = r^2 \rightarrow r = \sqrt{\frac{64}{\pi}} = \frac{8}{\sqrt{\pi}} = \frac{8}{\sqrt{\pi}} \times \frac{\sqrt{\pi}}{\sqrt{\pi}} = \frac{8\sqrt{\pi}}{\pi}$

6) **The answer is 72**

Length of the rectangle is: $\frac{5}{4} \times 16 = 20$, perimeter of rectangle is: $2 \times (20 + 16) = 72$

7) **The answer is $145°$**

The angle x and 35 are complementary angles. Therefore: $x + 35 = 180 \rightarrow$

$$x = 180° - 35° = 145°$$

8) The answer is 30

The sum of supplement angles is 180. Let x be that angle. Therefore, $x + 5x = 180$
$6x = 180$, divide both sides by 6: $x = 30$

9) The answer is -2

Solving Systems of Equations by Elimination: Multiply the first equation by (-2), then add it to the second equation.

$$\begin{array}{l} -2(2x + 5y = 11) \\ \underline{4x - 2y = -14} \end{array} \Rightarrow \begin{array}{l} -4x - 10y = -22 \\ 4x - 2y = -14 \end{array} \Rightarrow -12y = -36 \Rightarrow y = 3$$

Plug in the value of y into one of the equations and solve for x.

$2x + 5(3) = 11 \Rightarrow 2x + 15 = 11 \Rightarrow 2x = -4 \Rightarrow x = -2$

10) The answer is $60,000$

Three times of 24,000 is 72,000. One sixth of them cancelled their tickets. One sixth of 72,000 equals 12,000 $(\frac{1}{6} \times 72,000 = 12,000)$. 60,000 $(72,000 - 12,000 = 60,000)$ fans are attending this week.

11) The answer is $\frac{\sqrt{15}}{4}$

$sinA = \frac{1}{4} \Rightarrow$ Since $sin\theta = \frac{opposite}{hypotenuse}$, we have the following right triangle. Then:

$c = \sqrt{4^2 - 1^2} = \sqrt{16 - 1} = \sqrt{15}, cosA = \frac{\sqrt{15}}{4}$

12) The answer is 16π

The equation of a circle in standard form is: $(x - h)^2 + (y - k)^2 = r^2$, where r is the radius of the circle. In this circle the radius is 4. $r^2 = 16 \rightarrow r = 4$, $(x + 2)^2 + (y - 4)^2 = 16$, Area of a circle: $A = \pi r^2 = \pi(4)^2 = 16\pi$

13) The answer is 6.7×10^5

$670,000 = 6.7 \times 10^5$

14) The answer is 240

The ratio of boy to girls is $2:3$. Therefore, there are 2 boys out of 5 students. To find the answer, first divide the total number of students by 5, then multiply the result by 2.

$600 \div 5 = 120 \Rightarrow 120 \times 2 = 240$

15) The answer is 45

First, find the number. Let x be the number. Write the equation and solve for x. 150% of a number is 75, then: $1.5 \times x = 75 \Rightarrow x = 75 \div 1.5 = 50$, 90% of 50 is: $0.9 \times 50 = 45$

16) The answer is $\begin{bmatrix} -6 & 3 \\ 4 & -7 \end{bmatrix}$

First, find $2A$. $A = \begin{bmatrix} -1 & 2 \\ 1 & -2 \end{bmatrix}$; $2A = 2 \times \begin{bmatrix} -1 & 2 \\ 1 & -2 \end{bmatrix} = \begin{bmatrix} -2 & 4 \\ 2 & -4 \end{bmatrix}$

Now, solve for $2A - B$.

$2A - B = \begin{bmatrix} -2 & 4 \\ 2 & -4 \end{bmatrix} - \begin{bmatrix} 4 & 1 \\ -2 & 3 \end{bmatrix} = \begin{bmatrix} -2-4 & 4-1 \\ 2-(-2) & -4-3 \end{bmatrix} = \begin{bmatrix} -6 & 3 \\ 4 & -7 \end{bmatrix}$

17) The answer is $x \geq 5 \cup x \leq -1$

$x - 2 \geq 3 \rightarrow x \geq 3 + 2 \rightarrow x \geq 5$, Or $x - 2 \leq -3 \rightarrow x \leq -3 + 2 \rightarrow x \leq -1$

Then, solution is: $x \geq 5 \cup x \leq -1$

18) The answer is $\frac{8}{17}$

$\tan = \frac{opposite}{adjacent}$, and $\tan x = \frac{8}{15}$, therefore, the opposite side of the angle x is 8 and the adjacent side is 15. Let's draw the triangle.

Using Pythagorean theorem, we have: $a^2 + b^2 = c^2 \rightarrow 8^2 + 15^2 = c^2 \rightarrow 64 + 225 = c^2 \rightarrow c = 17$, $\sin x = \frac{opposite}{hypotenus} = \frac{8}{17}$

19) The answer is $x^{\frac{15}{4}}$

$(x^6)^{\frac{5}{8}} = x^{6 \times \frac{5}{8}} = x^{\frac{30}{8}} = x^{\frac{15}{4}}$

20) The answer are $0, -2, -3$

Frist factor the function: $f(x) = x^3 + 6x^2 + 8x = x(x+4)(x+2)$, To find the zeros, $f(x)$ should be zero. $f(x) = x(x+4)(x+2) = 0$, Therefore, the zeros are: $x = 0$, $(x+4) = 0 \Rightarrow x = -4$, $(x+2) = 0 \Rightarrow x = -2$

21) The answer is 2

$\sin^2 a + \cos^2 a = 1$, then: $x + 1 = 3$, $x = 2$

22) The answer is $\frac{y}{6}$

Solve for x. $\sqrt{6x} = \sqrt{y}$. Square both sides of the equation:

$(\sqrt{6x})^2 = (\sqrt{y})^2 \quad 6x = y; x = \frac{y}{6}$

23) The answer is 61.28

$average = \frac{sum\ of\ terms}{number\ of\ terms}$, The sum of the weight of all girls is: $18 \times 60 = 1,080\ kg$

The sum of the weight of all boys is: $32 \times 62 = 1,984\ kg$, The sum of the weight of all students is: $1,080 + 1,984 = 3,064\ kg$. $average = \frac{3,064}{50} = 61.28$

24) The answer is 36

Plug in the value of x and y. $x = 3$ and $y = -2$

$5(x - 2y) + (2 - x)^2 = 5(3 - 2(-2)) + (2 - 3)^2 = 5(3 + 4) + (-1)^2 = 35 + 1 = 36$

25) The answer is 15%

The question is this: 530.40 is what percent of 624?

Use percent formula: $part = \frac{percent}{100} \times whole$

$530.40 = \frac{percent}{100} \times 624 \Rightarrow 530.40 = \frac{percent \times 624}{100} \Rightarrow 53,040 = percent \times 624 \Rightarrow$

$percent = \frac{53,040}{624} = 85$. 530.40 is 85% of 624. Therefore, the discount is: $100\% - 85\% = 15\%$

26) The answer is $\frac{1}{2}$

The relationship among all sides of right triangle $30° - 60° - 90°$ is provided in the following triangle:

Sine of $30°$ equals to: $\frac{opposite}{hypotenus} = \frac{x}{2x} = \frac{1}{2}$

27) The answer is $\frac{3}{5} + i$

To simplify the fraction, multiply both numerator and denominator by i.

$\frac{5-3i}{-5i} \times \frac{i}{i} = \frac{5i-3i^2}{-5i^2}, i^2 - 1$, Then: $\frac{5i-3i^2}{-5i^2} = \frac{5i-3(-1)}{-5(-1)} = \frac{5i+3}{5} = \frac{5i}{5} + \frac{3}{5} = \frac{3}{5} + i$

28) The answer is 36

Let x be the smallest number. Then, these are the numbers: $x, x + 1, x + 2, x + 3, x + 4$

$average = \frac{sum\ of\ terms}{number\ of\ terms} \Rightarrow 38 = \frac{x+(x+1)+(x+2)+(x+3)+(x+4)}{5} \Rightarrow 38 = \frac{5x+10}{5} \Rightarrow$

$190 = 5x + 10 \Rightarrow 180 = 5x \Rightarrow x = 36$

29) The answer is $-\frac{1}{2}$

The equation of a line in slope intercept form is: $y = mx + b$. Solve for y. $4x - 2y = 12 \Rightarrow -2y = 12 - 4x \Rightarrow y = (12 - 4x) \div (-2) \Rightarrow y = 2x - 6$

The slope is 2. The slope of the line perpendicular to this line is:

$m_1 \times m_2 = -1 \Rightarrow 2 \times m_2 = -1 \Rightarrow m_2 = -\frac{1}{2}$

30) The answer is $\frac{2}{x^4} + 2$

$f(g(x)) = 2 \times (\frac{1}{x})^4 + 2 = \frac{2}{x^4} + 2$

ALEKS Mathematics Practice Test 2

1) The answer is $x^3 + 21x - 20$

Use FOIL (First, Out, In, Last), $(x-5)(x^2 + 5x + 4) = x^3 + 5x^2 + 4x - 5x^2 - 25x - 20 = x^3 + 21x - 20$

2) The answer is -38

Use PEMDAS (order of operation): $5 + 8 \times (-3) - [4 + 22 \times 5] \div 6 = 5 + 8 \times (-3) - [4 + 110] \div 6 = 5 + 8 \times (-3) - [114] \div 6 = 5 + (-24) - 19 = 5 + (-24) - 19 = 5 - 43 = -38$

3) The answer is $\dfrac{-x-3}{2x^2 - 10}$

Simplify: $\dfrac{\frac{1}{2} - \frac{x+5}{4}}{\frac{x^2}{2} - \frac{5}{2}} = \dfrac{\frac{1}{2} - \frac{x+5}{4}}{\frac{x^2-5}{2}} = \dfrac{2(\frac{1}{2} - \frac{x+5}{4})}{x^2 - 5} \Rightarrow$ Simplify: $\dfrac{1}{2} - \dfrac{x+5}{4} = \dfrac{-x-3}{4}$

then: $\dfrac{2(\frac{-x-3}{4})}{x^2 - 5} = \dfrac{\frac{-x-3}{2}}{x^2 - 5} = \dfrac{-x-3}{2(x^2-5)} = \dfrac{-x-3}{2x^2 - 10}$

4) The answer is 78

Number of squares equal to: $\frac{52 \times 12}{4 \times 2} = 13 \times 6 = 78$

5) The answer is $x \leq 5$

Simplify: $5 + 2x \leq 15 \Rightarrow 2x \leq 15 - 5 \Rightarrow 2x \leq 10 \Rightarrow x \leq 5$

6) The answer is \$635

$55 \times \$66 = \$3,630$ Payable amount is: $\$4,265 - \$3,630 = \$635$

7) The answer is $x^{\frac{5}{2}}$

$(x^4)^{\frac{5}{8}} = x^{4 \times \frac{5}{8}} = x^{\frac{20}{8}} = x^{\frac{5}{2}}$

8) The answer is 5231.6

Underline the tenth place: 2531.$\underline{5}$8245, Look to the right if it is 5 or bigger, add 1 to the underlined digit. Then, round up the decimal to 5231.6

9) The answer is 60

$25 \times \dfrac{x}{100} = 15 \Rightarrow 25 \times x = 1,500 \Rightarrow x = \dfrac{1,500}{25} = 60$

10) The answer is \$9.48

$\$44 - \$34.52 = \$9.48$

11) The answer is 45°

$90° + 45° = 135° \rightarrow 180° - 135° = 45°$

12) The answer is $(x - 4)(x - 3)$

$x^2 - 7x + 12 = (x - 4)(x - 3)$

13) The answer is $60ft$

The relationship among all sides of special right triangle

$30° - 60° - 90°$ is provided in this triangle:

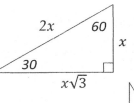

In this triangle, the opposite side of 30° angle is half of the hypotenuse.

Draw the shape of this question:

The latter is the hypotenuse. Therefore, the latter is $60\ ft$.

14) The answer is 5

$C = \sqrt{(x_A - x_B)^2 + (y - y_B)^2}$, $C = \sqrt{(1 - (-2))^2 + (3 - 7)^2} \rightarrow C = \sqrt{(3)^2 + (-4)^2} \rightarrow$
$C = \sqrt{9 + 16} \rightarrow C = \sqrt{25} = 5$

15) The answer is 0.0142

$\frac{2}{140} = \frac{1}{70} = 0.0142857143 \cong 0.0142$

16) The answer is 12

$\frac{a + b}{2} = 9 \Rightarrow a + b = 18$, $\frac{a + b + c}{3} = 10 \Rightarrow a + b + c = 30$

$18 + c = 30 \Rightarrow c = 30 - 18 = 12$

17) The answer is $-\frac{1}{2}, -3$

$x_{1,2} = \frac{-b \pm \sqrt{b^2 - 4ac}}{2a}$, $ax^2 + bx + c = 0 \Rightarrow 4x^2 + 14x + 6 = 0$ $\Rightarrow$ then: $a = 4$, $b = 14$ and
$c = 6$

$x = \frac{-1\ + \sqrt{14^2 - 4 \times 4 \times 6}}{2 \times 4} = -\frac{1}{2}$, $x = \frac{-14 - \sqrt{14^2 - 4 \times 4 \times 6}}{2 \times 4} = -3$

18) The answer is 13

$7^5 \times 7^8 = 7^{5+8} = 7^{13} = 7^x \rightarrow x = 13$

19) The answer is 33

$33 + 36 + 30 = 99$, $Average = \frac{99}{3} = 33$

20) The answer is $-1 + \sqrt{6}, -1 - \sqrt{6}$

$x_{1,2} = \dfrac{-b \pm \sqrt{b^2 - 4ac}}{2a}$, $ax^2 + bx + c = 0$, $x^2 + 2x - 5 = 0 \Rightarrow$ then: $a = 1$, $b = 2$ and $c = -5$

$x = \dfrac{-2 + \sqrt{2^2 - 4 \times 1 \times (-5)}}{2 \times 1} = -1 + \sqrt{6}$, $x = \dfrac{-2 - \sqrt{2^2 - 4 \times 1 \times (-5)}}{2 \times 1} = -1 - \sqrt{6}$

21) The answer is $(3, 3)$

$\begin{cases} -2x - y = -9 \\ 5x - 2y = 9 \end{cases} \Rightarrow$ Multiplication (-2) in first equation $\Rightarrow \begin{cases} 4x + 2y = 18 \\ 5x - 2y = 9 \end{cases}$

Add two equations together $\Rightarrow 9x = 27 \Rightarrow x = 3$ then: $y = 3$

22) The answer is 6

$|9 - (12 \div |2 - 6|)| = |9 - (12 \div |-4|)| = |9 - (12 \div 4)| = |9 - 3| = |6| = 6$

23) The answer is 32

$\log_2 x = 5$

Apply logarithm rule: $= log_b(b^a)$, $5 = log_2(2^5) = log_2(32)$

$log_2 x = log_2(32)$, When the logs have the same base:

$log_b(f(x)) = log_b(g(x)) \Rightarrow f(x) = g(x)$, then: $x = 32$

24) The answer is $\dfrac{14}{x^3}$

$\dfrac{x^3}{14} \Rightarrow$ reciprocal is : $\dfrac{14}{x^3}$

25) The answer is 60

Plug in 140 for F and then solve for C.

$C = \dfrac{5}{9}(F - 32) \Rightarrow C = \dfrac{5}{9}(140 - 32) \Rightarrow C = \dfrac{5}{9}(108) = 60$

26) The answer is $12i - 54$

We know that: $i = \sqrt{-1} \Rightarrow i^2 = -1$

$(-3 + 9i)(3 + 5i) = -9 - 15i + 27i + 45i^2 = -9 + 12i - 45 = 12i - 54$

27) The answer is $-\sqrt{3}$

$tan\dfrac{2\pi}{3} = \dfrac{sin\frac{2\pi}{3}}{cos\frac{2\pi}{3}} = \dfrac{\frac{\sqrt{3}}{2}}{-\frac{1}{2}} = -\sqrt{3}$

28) The answer is $\dfrac{5x-1}{x^2-x}$

$(\dfrac{f}{g})(x) = \dfrac{f(x)}{g(x)} = \dfrac{5x-1}{x^2-x}$

29) The answer is $(4, -9)$, $\sqrt{3}$

$(x-h)^2 + (y-k)^2 = r^2 \quad \Rightarrow$ center: (h, k) and radius: r

$(x-4)^2 + (y+7)^2 = 3 \quad \Rightarrow$ center: $(4, -9)$ and radius: $\sqrt{3}$

30) The answer is $(x+4)^2 + (y-2)^2 = 1$

Use formula of a circle in the coordinate plane: $(x-h)^2 + (y-k)^2 = r^2 \Rightarrow$ center: (h, k) and radius: r, center: $(-4, 2) \Rightarrow h = -4, k = 2$

circumference $= 2\pi \Rightarrow$ circumference $= 2\pi r = 2\pi \Rightarrow r = 1$

$(x+4)^2 + (y-2)^2 = 1$

www.EffortlessMath.com

... So Much More Online!

✓ FREE Math lessons

✓ More Math learning books!

✓ Mathematics Worksheets

✓ Online Math Tutors

Need a PDF version of this book?

Visit www.EffortlessMath.com

Receive the PDF version of this book or get another FREE book!

Thank you for using our Book!

Do you LOVE this book?

Then, you can get the PDF version of this book or another book absolutely FREE!

Please email us at:

info@EffortlessMath.com

for details.

Made in the USA
Coppell, TX
29 March 2021

52585361R00103